Sacred Hymns of the Book of Mormon

Angel Moroni Appearing to Joseph Smith
Henri Moser, 1909
Photographed by Joy Gough
Moser Family Collection
Used by permission.

Sacred Hymns of the Book of Mormon

Original Words and Music by

Marilyn Arnold and Maurine Ozment

with Lisa Farr

CFI

Springville, Utah

ISBN 13: 978-1-59955-215-6

Published by CFI, an imprint of Cedar Fort, Inc.
2373 W. 700 S., Springville, UT 84663
Distributed by Cedar Fort, Inc., www.cedarfort.com

Cover design by Jen Boss
Cover design © 2009 by Lyle Mortimer
Edited by Heidi Doxey

Printed in the United States of America

10 9 8 7 6 5 4 3

Printed on acid-free paper

Dedication

Humbly and gratefully we dedicate these sacred hymns to Mormon, Moroni, and Joseph Smith. Without their devotion and sacrifice, there would be no Book of Mormon.

Contents

Introduction

There is something miraculous about this book of hymns made from poems, poems written to be sung and also to be spoken. That it exists at all is a wonder to Maurine and to me still, as well as to her daughter Lisa. We all live on the edge of a lovely desert reserve where I often walk five or six days a week. For reasons I wasn't fully aware of at the time, I felt prompted to move in late 2005 to the area where Maurine had come a year or so earlier, after the death of her dear husband. We met in Relief Society in January 2006, as she was recovering from a serious and very complicated foot surgery. Lisa, who has since moved here with her family, was pushing her mother's wheelchair, and we happened to converge near the exit door at the meeting's conclusion.

A few months later, I learned that Maurine was an accomplished musician, having performed as a pianist on many concert stages and having composed and arranged countless pieces of music for both piano and choir (including some for various editions of the *Children's Song Book*). I also learned that, in addition to having received extensive training in music theory, she had served on college music faculties outside of Utah. She continues to teach private lessons to piano students.

When at last I heard Maurine splendidly play some of the finest and most difficult of piano compositions, I recognized that she was a woman of exceptional gifts. And then, as I was walking in the quiet of desert sand and sandstone in early June 2006, the thought came to me, out of the clear blue, that she and I should write a group of hymns based on the Book of Mormon. I have since realized that the thought came, not as a wild idea from my addled brain, but as a tender mercy from the Lord. I tell you, the reader, this so you will understand what this book means to its writer and its composer. I have long been a teacher and writer of prose, both fiction and non-fiction, and a teacher of poems and other writings; but I have never supposed that I was a poet (except at heart). And what have I done but write thirty-two poems and dared to offer them for publication?

The amazing thing is that Maurine caught the spirit of this idea from day one, perhaps because we both love the Book of Mormon more than any other written text on earth. It speaks to us, as our concluding hymn avows, and I unashamedly testify here that these hymns were written and composed with the help of heaven. That is a bold statement, and I don't make it lightly, or out of pridefulness, but out of the deepest humility and gratitude. Simply put, we could not have done this on our own, nor did we do this on our own. In preparing these hymns, we have been incredibly blessed, and we have drawn closer to the source of all blessings. With Ammon, we shout that in our God we rejoice, and give thanks every day for His great goodness.

Most certainly, we could not have done this without Lisa, who moved here with her family at just the moment we had need of her. Lisa is a fine musician herself, as is her husband, and she is also a whiz on the computer—which could never be said of either Maurine or me. Like us, Lisa caught the spirit of this work, and she has spent countless hours transforming penciled music manuscripts and words into pages of printed hymns. As we have rewritten, revised, edited, and refined many times over, Lisa has taken our changes and entered them and reprinted the revised hymns. Not once has she complained or balked, and she has made many helpful suggestions. We also owe a debt of gratitude to Bonnie Ballif-Spanville, a dear friend and colleague as well as a wonderfully gifted musician and trained vocalist. Her reading of a good many of these hymns, both early and late in the process, and her extremely helpful suggestions, have proved invaluable. She taught us to see how the hymns could be made stronger and more singable. Moreover, she has given us unwavering encouragement and support.

And now, a word about the hymns themselves, and our reasons for writing them. As I suggested above, we wrote these hymns out of love for the Book of Mormon and the very real people who live in its pages, but also out of love for the Church, for the gospel, and for Joseph Smith who invested his very being in the translation of the book. Finally, and most consequentially, we wrote out of deep love and gratitude for Jesus Christ, of whom the book testifies so powerfully we wonder that anyone could read it and doubt the reality of the Savior and His atoning sacrifice, much less His personal appearance to His people in the western hemisphere.

Some of the hymns came to us virtually as direct inspiration, particularly the first hymn we wrote, "The Waters of Mormon." It doesn't appear first in the collection, but it arrived as a pure gift and remains one of our favorites to this day. We readily and happily took it as a bit of divine encouragement, perhaps a signal of approval of what we were setting out to do. Others did not come so easily, and many have been worked and reworked and reworked. But we learned much in that process, including the power of unceasing prayer for guidance. (The matter of the hymns was even an addendum to nearly every prayer I offered over food for many months!) "Lehite Women" is another favorite, and it came to us near the end of the work. It answered a very real need for us, as women, to contemplate the role of the incredible women who, like the men in their lives, gave much and suffered much. We found, too, a tender kinship with these dear sisters of long ago, these sisters of Lehite lineage, both Nephite and Lamanite.

Some of the hymns are straightforward and simple, suitable especially for use in the home or at firesides or informal gatherings. Others are a bit more ambitious, perhaps, and might well tempt a choir director to choose them for special numbers. Some would also serve well as duets, trios, quartets, and solos—instrumental as well as vocal. Appreciative choirs, trios, and vocal, flute, and violin soloists have performed some already. The ordering of the hymns is not strictly chronological, though in a broad sense the book moves that way. The hymns seemed of themselves to suggest an order, and again, we followed inspiration. We believe that you will detect subtle groupings, and we hope they will make some sense to you, with opening and closing hymns calling us to read and study the Book of Mormon with a believing mind and heart. One group of hymns is focused specifically on the Savior—visions of Him, prophecies of His coming, and events that transpired during His ministry among the blessed survivors who witnessed His coming to the New World.

This then, is our hope: that you will venture to sing these hymns in your homes and wherever else Saints and neighbors meet. We hope that you will see these hymns, with us, as a way to remind ourselves of, and relive, memorable events and teachings in the Book of Mormon. Perhaps more important is our hope that, with us, you will arrive at a heightened appreciation of the profound application of these teachings to each of us individually as well as to all of us as a body of Saints in latter days.

You will notice that we have included the poems as separate entities that can, in good conscience, be read and enjoyed on their own. It is not required that anyone who receives this book has to sing them. Of course, we are partial to the combined words and music and highly recommend the two in tandem—even for those who, like me, can do little more than make a joyful noise unto the Lord.

Marilyn Arnold

Hymns

1. From the Dust Shall They Come

2 Nephi 26:14–17; 2 Nephi 27:6–11, 13, 29; Mormon 8:16, 23, 26, 35

From the dust shall they come, from the earth shall they rise,
the words of the righteous who slumber.
From the dust whisper they, from the ground will they speak
words written of old, without number.

Yes, the words of a book shall the Lord God bring forth,
the words of the sleepers now spoken.
Then the eyes of the blind and the ears of the deaf
shall open, the long silence broken.

From the dust shall they cry, and their words will shine forth
from darkness, and none can delay it.
When the power of God reaches out to a man,
a book shall come forth; none can stay it.

Out of earth shall they come, by the hand of the Lord,
the words of dead saints gone before us.
They shall burst into light as they cry from the dust,
the words ever true, ever glorious.

1. From the Dust Shall They Come

2 Nephi 26:14–17; 2 Nephi 27:6–11, 13, 29;
Mormon 8:16, 23, 26, 35

Fervently ♩= 66
1. From the dust shall they come, from the earth shall they rise, the
2. Yes, the words of a book shall the Lord God bring forth, the
3. From the dust shall they cry, and their words will shine forth from
4. Out of earth shall they come, by the hand of the Lord, the
3
words of the right - eous who slum - ber. From the dust whis - per they, from the
words of the sleep - ers now spo - ken. Then the eyes of the blind and the
dark - ness, and none can de - lay it. When the pow - er of God reach - es
words of dead saints gone be - fore us. They shall burst in - to light as they
6
ground will they speak words writ - ten of old, with - out num - ber.
ears of the deaf shall o - pen, the long si - lence bro - ken.
out to a man, a book shall come forth; none can stay it.
cry from the dust, the words ev - er true, ev - er glo - rious.

Text: Marilyn Arnold | Music: Maurine B. Ozment

2. Receive These Words with Grateful Hearts

Jacob 4

Receive these words with grateful hearts, these words from plates
of gold,
Engraven here at God's command by prophets, seers of old.
We write for you in later times as witness of our faith
That Christ, our Lord, Begotten Son, would come to conquer death.

Refrain

Behold, O how glorious are the works of the Lord,
Unsearchable the depths of His being.
No man knows His mysteries, no man knows His ways,
Except he transcend mortal seeing.

We knew of Christ before His birth, long centuries before.
His glory filled our lives with hope; we worshiped and adored.
And now in faith unshaken, firm, we testify of Him
Whose word breaks forth to fill the earth with truth, man's soul
to win.

2. Receive These Words with Grateful Hearts

Jacob 4

Joyfully ♩= 72
Unison
1. Re - ceive these words with grate-ful hearts, these words from plates of gold, En-grav-en here at God's com-mand by pro - phets, seers of old. We write for you in lat - er times as wit-ness of our
2. We knew of Christ be - fore His birth, long cen - tu - ries be- fore. His glo - ry filled our lives with hope; we wor - shiped and a- dored. And now in faith un-shak-en, firm, we tes - ti - fy of
6
10

Text: Marilyn Arnold

Music: Maurine B. Ozment

Receive These Words with Grateful Hearts

14
faith That Christ, our Lord, Be-got-ten Son, would come to con-quer death.
Him Whose word breaks forth to fill the earth with truth, man's soul to win.
19
Refrain
Harmony
Be - hold, O how glo - ri - ous are the works of the Lord,
24
Un - search - a - ble the depths of His be - ing.

Text: Marilyn Arnold

Music: Maurine B. Ozment

Receive These Words with Grateful Hearts

28
No man knows His mys - ter - ies, no man knows His
31
ways, Ex - cept he tran - scend mor - tal see - ing.

Text: Marilyn Arnold

Music: Maurine B. Ozment

3. *My Father, Great Lehi*

1 Nephi; 2 Nephi 1–4

My father, great Lehi, my father—a man whom I love and revere—
He taught me by word and example of sacred things precious
and dear.
The Lord spoke and Lehi consented; he gave up his wealth and
his lands
To live in remote isolation, no more to see home place and friends.

The Lord trusted Lehi, my father, to travel across the broad sea
Where waited a land with a promise, preserved for the righteous
and free.
A prophet with vision and wisdom, opposed by his two older sons;
Yet father, great Lehi, my father, endured 'til his mission was done.

My pillar of strength and my comfort, a man of the ages he was.
A holy man, destined for hardship, for sacrifice, sorrow, and loss,
He knew all along that the evil was there that we might know
the good.
I, Nephi, am blessed by his memory; I, Nephi, in faith will abide.

3. My Father, Great Lehi

1 Nephi; 2 Nephi 1–4

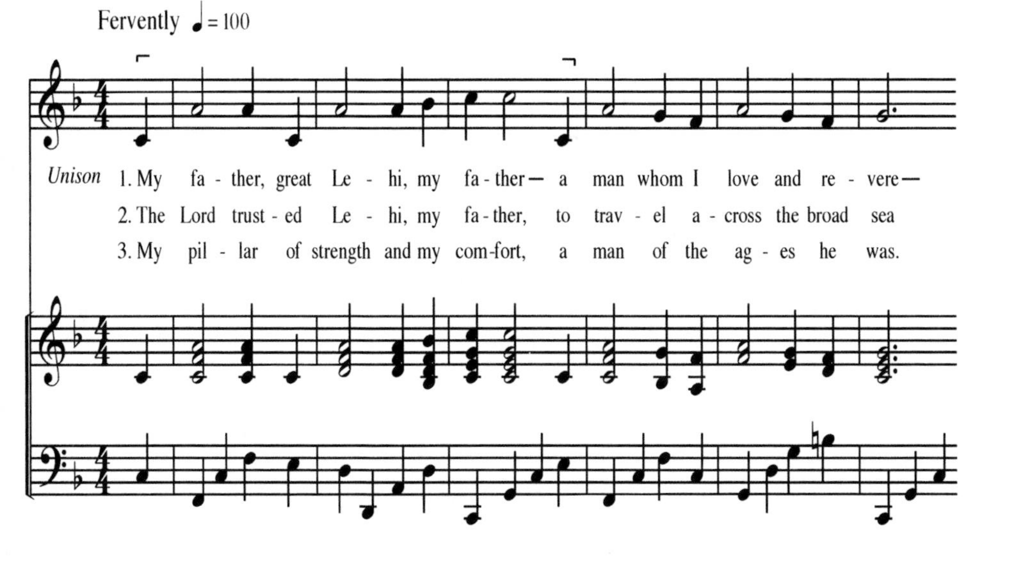
Fervently ♩ = 100
Unison
1. My fa - ther, great Le - hi, my fa - ther— a man whom I love and re - vere—
2. The Lord trust - ed Le - hi, my fa - ther, to trav - el a - cross the broad sea
3. My pil - lar of strength and my com-fort, a man of the ag - es he was.

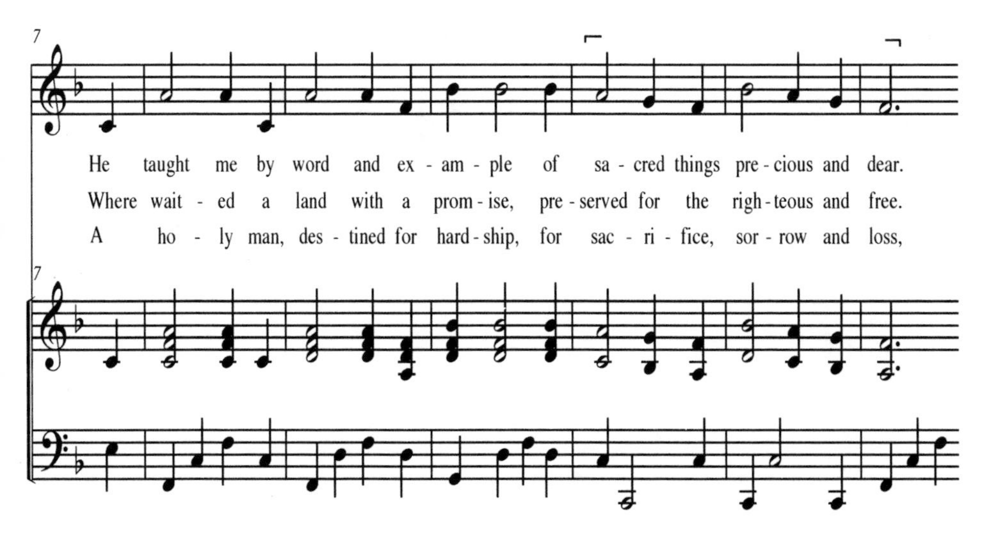
7
He taught me by word and ex - am - ple of sa - cred things pre - cious and dear.
Where wait - ed a land with a prom - ise, pre - served for the righ - teous and free.
A ho - ly man, des - tined for hard - ship, for sac - ri - fice, sor - row and loss,
7

Text: Marilyn Arnold

Music: Maurine B. Ozment

My Father, Great Lehi

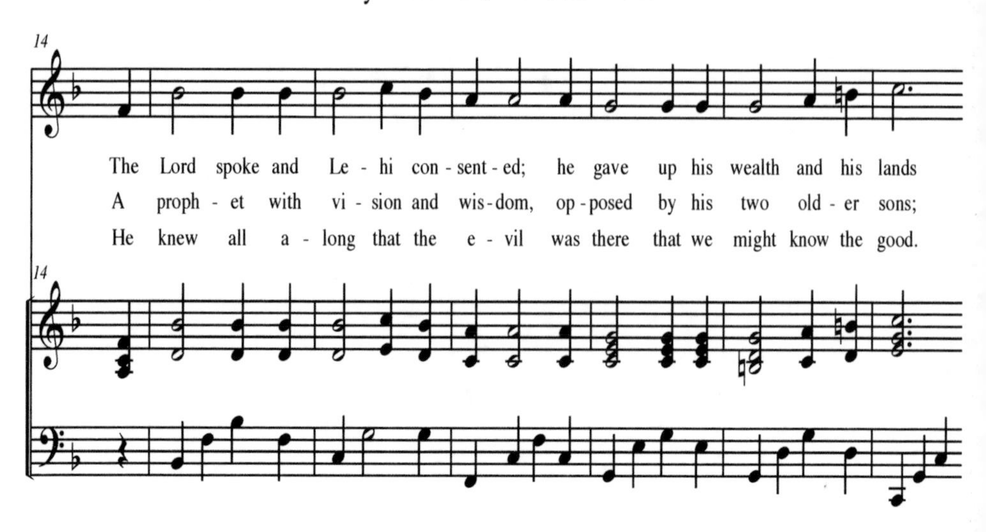
14
The Lord spoke and Le - hi con - sent - ed; he gave up his wealth and his lands
A proph - et with vi - sion and wis - dom, op - posed by his two old - er sons;
He knew all a - long that the e - vil was there that we might know the good.
14

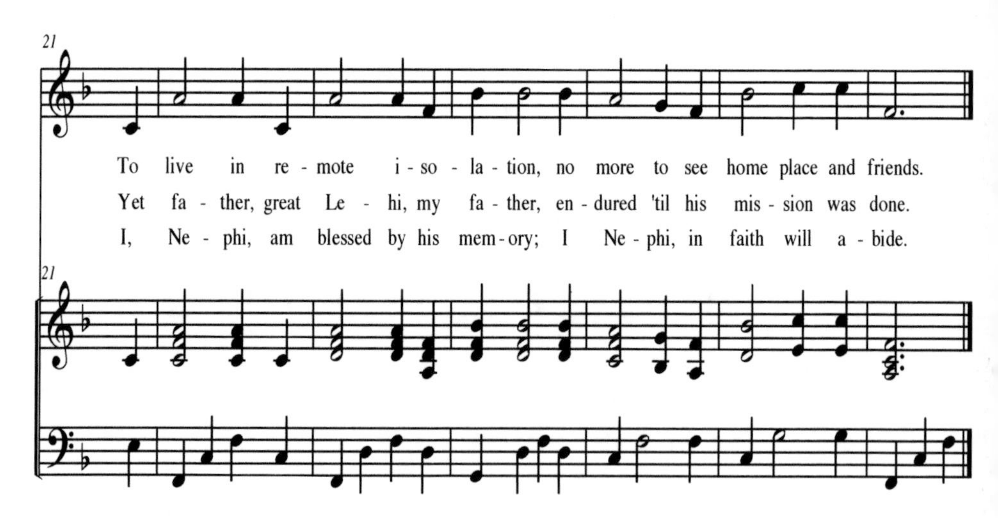
21
To live in re - mote i - so - la - tion, no more to see home place and friends.
Yet fa - ther, great Le - hi, my fa - ther, en - dured 'til his mis - sion was done.
I, Ne - phi, am blessed by his mem - ory; I Ne - phi, in faith will a - bide.
21

Text: Marilyn Arnold

Music: Maurine B. Ozment

4. Lehite Women

The Book of Mormon All-inclusive

Nephite woman, come tell me your story,
    Come alive in my mind and my heart.
Let me ponder your life as an exile,
    the trials that you faced from the start.
Nephite woman, your image eludes me
    as I search sacred verse for your name.
You are absent from view, yet your nearness
    I feel, and your strength, just the same.

Like your sister, the Lamanite woman,
    you endured endless wars, endless strife.
And like her, you knew moments of gladness;
    like her, you were mother and wife.
Lehite women, I weep for your sorrows,
    for your stories that never were told.
Still, I sense you behind every chapter,
    your presence like slivers of gold.

4. Lehite Women

The Book of Mormon All-inclusive

Thoughtfully ♩ = 88
Unison
1. Ne - phite wom - an, come tell me your sto - ry,
2. Like your sis - ter, the La - man - ite wom - an,
6
Come a - live in my mind and my heart.
You en - dured end - less wars, end - less strife.
10
Let me pon - der your life as an ex - ile,
And like her, you knew mo - ments of glad - ness;
15
The trials that you faced from the start.
Like her, you were moth - er and wife.

Text: Marilyn Arnold

Music: Maurine B. Ozment

Lehite Women

20
Optional descant
Harmony
Ne - phite wom - an, your im - age e - ludes me
Le - hite wom - en, I weep for your sor - rows,
24
As I search sa - cred verse for your name.
For your sto - ries that nev - er were told.
28
You are ab - sent from view, yet your near - ness
Still, I sense you be - hind eve - ry chap - ter,

Text: Marilyn Arnold

Music: Maurine B. Ozment

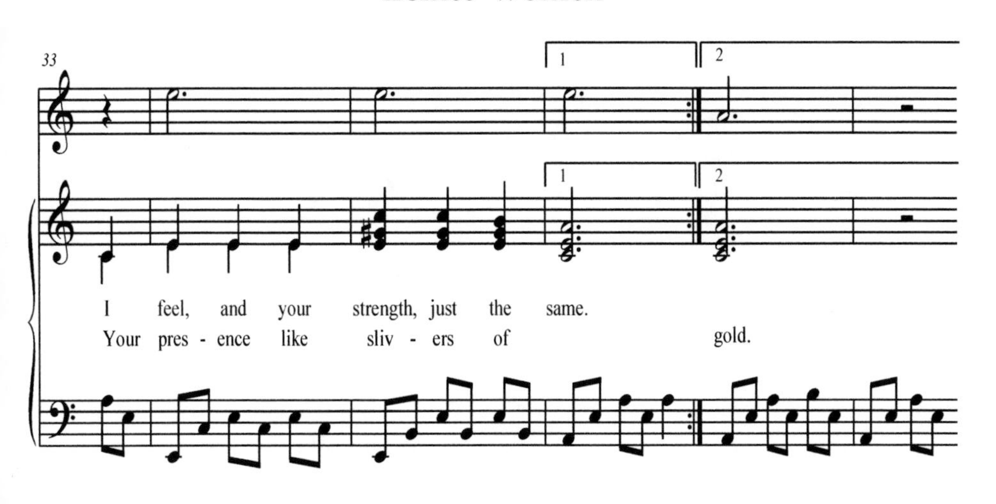
33
1
2
I feel, and your strength, just the same.
Your pres - ence like sliv - ers of gold.

39
ritard
8va
Your pres - ence, like sliv - ers of gold.

Text: Marilyn Arnold

Music: Maurine B. Ozment

5. Nephi's Psalm

2 Nephi 4:16–35

Peace, peace, come find me now, discover all my sorrow.
Gone my father, gone to dust, no strength from him to borrow.
Why, why, sink I in sin? Why now to grief surrender?
Why succumb to fear and pain when God is nigh, so tender?

Night, night, though once you brought vast scenes so full of wonder—
Look! The angel cried aloud, with voice that rang like thunder—
Gone, gone, days precious, rare, when brothers yet repented.
Gone my hope for their return, but still on God dependent.

Wake, wake, my soul awake! No more with anguish ridden.
Joy is thine, my heart rejoice, let anger be forbidden.
Cry, cry, cry to the Lord, come praise His name unending.
Cry in praise of Him, my Rock, before Him ever bending.

Hear, hear, I beg Thee, Lord, with heart contrite, beseeching;
Hear my vow, in Thee I trust, my soul toward Thee reaching.
Lord, God, save Thee my soul, from wicked foes deliver.
Lord, make straight my every path, encircle me forever.

5. Nephi's Psalm

2 Nephi 4:16–35

Thoughtfully ♩= 96
1. Peace, peace, come find me now, dis - cov - er all my sor - row.
2. Night, night, though once you brought vast scenes so full of won - der—
3. Wake, wake, my soul a - wake! No more with an - guish rid - den.
4. Hear, hear, I beg Thee, Lord, with heart con - trite, be - seech - ing;
Gone my fa - ther, gone to dust, no strength from him to bor - row.
Look! the an - gel cried a - loud, with voice that rang like thun - der—
Joy is thine, my heart re - joice, let an - ger be for - bid - den.
Hear my vow, in Thee I trust, my soul to - ward Thee reach - ing.
Why, why, sink I in sin? Why now to grief sur - ren - der?
Gone, gone, days pre - cious, rare, when broth - ers yet re - pent - ed.
Cry, cry, cry to the Lord, come praise his name un - end - ing.
Lord, God, save Thee my soul, from wick - ed foes de - liv - er.
Why suc - cumb to fear and pain when God is nigh, so ten - der?
Gone my hope for their re - turn, but still on God de - pen - dent.
Cry in praise of Him, my Rock, be - fore Him ev - er bend - ing.
Lord, make straight my eve - ry path, en - cir - cle me for - ev - er.

Text: Marilyn Arnold

Music: Maurine B. Ozment

6. With Hungry Soul

Enos 1

With hungry soul I knelt in prayer, alone in forest dim.
All day I cried unceasingly to God, to plead with Him.
All night I raised my voice and asked that He my soul
would cleanse,
And then His answer came at last; He swept away my sins.

"Thy faith hath made thee whole," He said, "thy faith in
Christ unseen.
Whatever thou shalt ask in faith, believing, thou shalt win."
The power of God called me to preach, to teach and prophesy;
And so I have, and now I go to where He waits on high.

6. With Hungry Soul

Enos 1

Earnestly ♩= 66
1. With hun - gry soul I knelt in prayer, a - lone in for - est dim. All day I
2. "Thy faith hath made thee whole," He said, "thy faith in Christ un - seen. What-ev - er
cried un-ceas-ing - ly to God, to plead with Him. All night I raised my voice and asked that
thou shalt ask in faith, be - liev - ing, thou shalt win." The power of God called me to preach, to
He my soul would cleanse, And then His an - swer came at last; He swept a - way my sins.
teach and proph - e - sy; And so I have, and now I go to where He waits on high.
5
11

Text: Marilyn Arnold

Music: Maurine B. Ozment

7. Abinadi, Abinadi

Mosiah 11–18

Abinadi, Abinadi, could I be brave like you?
Abinadi, Abinadi, could I be strong and true?
Could I stand up to wicked men and testify of Christ?
Could I refuse to call words back, regardless of the price?

Abinadi, Abinadi, one man your doctrine heard;
Abinadi, Abinadi, one man was deeply stirred.
Would I have known you spoke the truth, as Alma knew that day?
Would I have written all your words, would I have knelt to pray?

Abinadi, Abinadi, you published peace, indeed;
Abinadi, Abinadi, you spurned King Noah's creed.
You rose from scorn and martyr's fire to join the throngs above
Who faithful proved and now rejoice in God's redeeming love.

Abinadi, Abinadi, you've pointed me the way.
Abinadi, Abinadi, I'll follow and obey.
I'll keep the faith for which you died and hold your memory dear;
May I ascend one day to Christ and find you waiting there.

7. Abinadi, Abinadi

Mosiah 11–18

With conviction ♩ = 88
1. A - bin - a - di, A - bin - a - di, could I be brave like you?
2. A - bin - a - di, A - bin - a - di, one man your doc - trine heard;
3. A - bin - a - di, A - bin - a - di, you pub - lished peace, in - deed;
4. A - bin - a - di, A - bin - a - di, you've point - ed me the way.
5
A - bin - a - di, A - bin - a - di, could I be strong and true?
A - bin - a - di, A - bin - a - di, one man was deep - ly stirred.
A - bin - a - di, A - bin - a - di, you spurned King No - ah's creed.
A - bin - a - di, A - bin - a - di, I'll fol - low and o - bey.
10
Could I stand up to wick - ed men and tes - ti - fy of Christ?
Would I have known you spoke the truth, as Al - ma knew that day?
You rose from scorn and mar - tyr's fire to join the throngs a - bove
I'll keep the faith for which you died and hold your mem - ory dear;
15
Could I re - fuse to call words back, re - gard - less of the price?
Would I have writ - ten all your words, would I have knelt to pray?
Who faith - ful proved and now re - joice in God's re - deem - ing love.
May I as - cend one day to Christ and find you wait - ing there.

Text: Marilyn Arnold

Music: Maurine B. Ozment

8. The Waters of Mormon

Mosiah 18

What power they knew, what sweet delight
On rising from that fountain pure,
When Alma lifted them washed clean
From Mormon's waters, meek and sure.

Their head was Christ, they knew it now.
From doubt and fear they found release
And cov'nant vowed before their Lord
To love and serve in holy peace.

Each other's burdens they would bear
And freely give to those in need—
Hearts knit together one in faith,
And daily bend their knees to plead.

The Spirit's joy filled every heart,
Each soul was touched by God's own grace.
They strove to live by His command
That they one day might see His face.

8. The Waters of Mormon

With Violin or Flute

Mosiah 18

Joyfully ♩=96
Obligato verses 3 and 4
1. What pow - er they knew, what sweet de - light On ris - ing from that foun - tain pure, When Al - ma lift - ed them washed clean From Mor - mon's wa - ters, meek and sure.
2. Their head was Christ, they knew it now. From doubt and fear they found re - lease And cov' - nant vowed be- fore their Lord To love and serve in ho - ly peace.
3. Each oth - er's bur - dens they would bear And free - ly give to those in need — Hearts knit to - geth - er one in faith, And dai - ly bend their knees to plead.

Text: Marilyn Arnold

Music: Maurine B. Ozment

The Waters of Mormon

17
26
4. The Spir - it's joy filled eve - ry heart, Each soul was
32
touched by God's own grace. They strove to live by
37
His com - mand That they one day might see His face.

Text: Marilyn Arnold

Music: Maurine B. Ozment

8. The Waters of Mormon

Mosiah 18

Joyfully ♩=96
1. What pow - er they knew, what sweet de - light On ris - ing
2. Their head was Christ, they knew it now. From doubt and
3. Each oth - er's bur - dens they would bear And free - ly
4. The Spir - it's joy filled eve - ry heart, Each soul was

6
from that foun - tain pure, When Al - ma lift - ed
fear they found re - lease And cov' - nant vowed be-
give to those in need — Hearts knit to - geth - er
touched by God's own grace. They strove to live by

11
them washed clean From Mor - mon's wa - ters, meek and sure.
fore their Lord To love and serve in ho - ly peace.
one in faith, And dai - ly bend their knees to plead.
His com - mand That they one day might see His face.

Text: Marilyn Arnold

Music: Maurine B. Ozment

9. I Am Born Now of God

(The Younger Alma's Conversion)
Mosiah 27; Alma 36

I am born now of God, of the Spirit I'm born,
I am snatched from the darkest abyss.
The angel's rebuke wracked my soul with my sins
'Til the Lord changed my torment to bliss.

I am born now of God, of the Spirit I'm born,
For I cried to Lord Jesus in pain.
Have mercy, I cried, blessed Jesus forgive;
Blessed Jesus, come shatter death's chains.

I am born now of God, of the Spirit I'm born,
Oh what rapture, what joy, fills my heart!
What light I beheld, and what vision of praise,
And what promise, what hope, it imparts.

9. I Am Born Now of God

(The Younger Alma's Conversion)

Mosiah 27; Alma 36

With conviction ♩= 96
1. I am born now of God, of the Spir - it I'm born, I am
2. I am born now of God, of the Spir - it I'm born, For I
3. I am born now of God, of the Spir - it I'm born, Oh what
5
snatched from the dark - est a - byss. The an - gel's re - buke wracked my
cried to Lord Je - sus in pain. Have mer - cy, I cried, bless - ed
rap - ture, what joy, fills my heart! What light I be - held, and what
8
soul with my sins 'Til the Lord changed my tor - ment to bliss.
Je - sus for - give; Bless - ed Je - sus, come shat - ter death's chains.
vi - sion of praise, And what prom - ise, what hope, it im - parts.

Text: Marilyn Arnold

Music: Maurine B. Ozment

10. O That I Were an Angel

Alma 28

I'd speak with the trump, with the trump of our God,
with voice that could shake all the earth.
With thunderous voice I would cry to each soul,
repent, O repent, and hear truth.

Refrain

O that I were an angel, a bright bearer of news—
O if I had the wish of my heart,
O I'd shout the glad tidings of heavenly joy,
O the word, yes, the word I'd impart.

My voice would ring out if an angel I were,
to tell of redemption and bliss;
Redemption that banishes sorrow and pain,
I'd shout it if I had my wish.

But I am a man, and do sin in my wish;
my calling I'll gladly fulfill.
How blessed it is just to teach as a man,
to serve in accord with His will.

10. O That I Were an Angel

Alma 28

Joyfully ♩ = 84
1. I'd speak with the trump, with the trump of our God, with voice that could shake all the earth. With thun - der - ous voice I would cry to each soul, re - pent, O re - pent, and hear truth.
2. My voice would ring out if an an - gel I were, to tell of re - demp - tion and bliss; Re - demp - tion that ban - ish - es sor - row and pain, I'd shout it if I had my wish.
3. But I am a man, and do sin in my wish; my call - ing I'll glad - ly ful - fill. How bless - ed it is just to teach as a man, to serve in ac - cord with His will.
3
6

Text: Marilyn Arnold

Music: Maurine B. Ozment

O That I Were an Angel

9
Refrain
O that I were an an - gel, a bright bear - er of news —
O that I
14
O if I had the wish of my heart, O I'd shout the glad tid-ings of
O if I
19
heav - en - ly joy, O the word, yes, the word I'd im - part.
O the word,

Text: Marilyn Arnold

Music: Maurine B. Ozment

11. I Will Believe

(Prayer of the Lamanite King)
Alma 22

He heard Aaron's words, the great Lamanite king,
the words of redemption and hope.
They touched the king's heart and he hungered for truth;
in meekness he fervently spoke:

Refrain
"If you say that God lives, I'll believe, I'll believe,"
Cried the king as he bowed to the ground.
"I'll believe what you teach, I'll believe, I'll believe;
I was lost, I was lost, now I'm found."

"Oh, what need I do to partake of this joy,
this joy in the Christ who will come
To save men from sin and to conquer the grave,
embrace us and gather us home?"

He fell to his knees as he lifted his voice,
"Blessed God, if indeed you are there;
I'll give up my crown, my possessions, my sins,
to know Thee and joy in Thy care."

So uttered the king, in humility bent,
in grief and regret for the past;
So uttered the king as he pled with his God
to guide him home safely at last.

11. I Will Believe

(Prayer of the Lamanite King)

Alma 22

With conviction ♩=96
1. He heard Aar - on's words, the great La - man - ite king, the
2. "Oh, what need I do to par - take of this joy, this
3. He fell to his knees as he lift - ed his voice, "Blessed
4. So ut - tered the king, in hu - mil - i - ty bent, in
5
words of re - demp - tion and hope. They touched the king's heart and he
joy in the Christ who will come To save men from sin and to
God, if in - deed you are there; I'll give up my crown, my pos -
grief and re - gret for the past; So ut - tered the king as he
10
hun - gered for truth; in meek - ness he fer - vent - ly spoke:
con - quer the grave, em - brace us and gath - er us home?"
ses - sions, my sins, to know Thee and joy in Thy care."
pled with his God to guide him home safe - ly at last.

Text: Marilyn Arnold

Music: Maurine B. Ozment

I Will Believe

15
Refrain
"If you say that God lives, I'll be - lieve, I'll be - lieve," Cried the
20
king as he bowed to the ground. "I'll be - lieve what you teach, I'll be -
26
lieve, I'll be - lieve; I was lost, I was lost, now I'm found."

Text: Marilyn Arnold

Music: Maurine B. Ozment

12. Our Swords Are Made Bright

(Lamanites Bury Their Swords)
Alma 23–24

Anti-Nephi-Lehi speaks to his people

Our swords are made bright, let us hide them away;
Our swords, let us stain them no more.
Our swords are washed clean through the blood of the Lamb,
Now bury them deep, I implore.

The guilt of our hearts God has taken away,
Our guilt through the gift of His Son.
The blood we have shed He forgives and forgets,
Our works of destruction are done.

We'll give up our lives, yes, we'll kneel and be slain,
We'll take not a sword in our hand.
The truth we have found, and to truth we will cling;
Our souls, not our lives, we'll defend.

A thousand were slain in the battle that day;
Not one raised a weapon to fight.
They went to their God ever faithful and just,
With thanks in their hearts for the light.

A thousand were saved in the battle that day,
A thousand and more of the foe
Whose hearts were there touched by the valor of those
Who died without fear, without woe.

12. Our Swords Are Made Bright

(Lamanites Bury Their Swords)

Alma 23–24

With dignity ♩ = 66

Anti-Nephi-Lehi speaks to his people:

1. Our swords are made bright, let us hide them a - way; Our
2. The guilt of our hearts God has ta - ken a - way, Our
3. We'll give up our lives, yes, we'll kneel and be slain, We'll

3
swords, let us stain them no more. Our swords are washed clean through the
guilt through the gift of His Son. The blood we have shed He for -
take not a sword in our hand. The truth we have found, and to

6
blood of the Lamb, Now bur - y them deep, I im - plore.
gives and for - gets, Our works of de - struc - tion are done.
truth we will cling; Our souls, not our lives, we'll de - fend.

Text: Marilyn Arnold

Music: Maurine B. Ozment

Our Swords Are Made Bright

Solemnly ♩= 84

Narrator speaks:

9
4. A thou - sand were slain in the bat - tle that day; Not

14
one raised a weap - on to fight. They went to their God ev - er

19
faith - ful and just, With thanks in their hearts for the light.

Text: Marilyn Arnold

Music: Maurine B. Ozment

Our Swords Are Made Bright

With dignity ♩=66
24
5. A thou - sand were saved in the bat - tle that day, A
27
thou - sand and more of the foe Whose hearts were there touched by the
30
val - or of those Who died with - out fear, with - out woe.

Text: Marilyn Arnold

Music: Maurine B. Ozment

12. Our Swords Are Made Bright

Male Quartet

(Lamanites Bury Their Swords)

Alma 23–24

With dignity ♩ = 66

Anti-Nephi-Lehi speaks to his people:

1. Our swords are made bright, let us hide them a - way; Our
2. The guilt of our hearts God has ta - ken a - way, Our
3. We'll give up our lives, yes, we'll kneel and be slain, We'll
Piano
3
swords, let us stain them no more. Our swords are washed clean through the
guilt through the gift of His Son. The blood we have shed He for-
take not a sword in our hand. The truth we have found, and to
Pno.

Text: Marilyn Arnold

Music: Maurine B. Ozment

Our Swords Are Made Bright
6
blood of the Lamb, Now bur - y them deep, I im - plore.
gives and for - gets, Our works of de - struc - tion are done.
truth we will cling; Our souls, not our lives, we'll de - fend.
Pno.
Solemnly ♩ = 84
Narrator:
9
(Solo) 4. A thou - sand were slain in the bat - tle that day; Not
Pno.
14
one raised a weap - on to fight. They went to their
Pno.

Text: Marilyn Arnold

Music: Maurine B. Ozment

Our Swords Are Made Bright

God ev - er faith - ful and just, With thanks in their hearts for the light.
Pno.
With dignity ♩ = 66
24
(All) 5. A thou - sand were saved in the bat - tle that day, A
Pno.
27
thou - sand and more of the foe Whose hearts were there touched by the
Pno.

Text: Marilyn Arnold

Music: Maurine B. Ozment

Our Swords Are Made Bright

30
val - or of those Who died with - out fear, with - out woe.
Pno.

Text: Marilyn Arnold

Music: Maurine B. Ozment

13. In My God I Do Rejoice

(Ammon Exults in the Great Lamanite Conversion)
Alma 26

My heart is brim with joy; in my God I do rejoice.
In His praise I will lift up my voice.
    In His praise I lift my voice.
    We have reason to praise Him forever.

They sing redeeming love, who were once fast bound for hell—
In His love and His light e'er to dwell.
    In His light fore'er to dwell,
    They will dwell in His light now forever.

It's God I do extol when my joy leads me to boast.
He is wise, He is loving, and just.
    He is wise and kind and just,
    And all power is His, His forever.

Redeemed am I from woe, and our brothers saved from sin.
Render thanks to the skies and laud Him.
    Give Him thanks, O give Him laud;
    Come extol Him and praise Him forever.

13. In My God I Do Rejoice

(Ammon Exults in the Great Lamanite Conversion)

Alma 26

Jubilantly ♩ = 104
1. My heart is brim with joy; in my God I do re - joice.
2. They sing re - deem - ing love, who were once fast bound for hell—
3. It's God I do ex - tol when my joy leads me to boast.
4. Re - deemed am I from woe, and our bro - thers saved from sin.
5
In His praise I will lift up my voice. In His praise I lift my
In His love and His light e'er to dwell. In His light for - e'er to
He is wise, He is lov - ing, and just. He is wise and kind and
Ren - der thanks to the skies and laud Him. Give Him thanks, O give Him
10
voice. We have rea - son to praise Him for - ev - er.
dwell, They will dwell in His light now for - ev - er.
just, And all pow - er is His, His for - ev - er.
laud; Come ex - tol Him and praise Him for - ev - er.

Text: Marilyn Arnold

Music: Maurine B. Ozment

14. King Benjamin

Mosiah 3–5

King Benjamin, a holy man, in righteousness he reigned.
By strength of faith and might of will, the victory he gained.
On plains of war and fields of peace he crushed the serpent's head;
With wisdom, hope, and selfless life—with virtue pure he led.

"Put off the natural man," he taught. "Become a child once more—
Submissive, meek, and full of love. Give freely to the poor,
For we are beggars, every one, unable to repay
The God who pours His bounties forth to bless us every day."

With voice as one the people cried, "We do, we do believe!
Our hearts are changed, our souls reborn. No more to be deceived
By Satan's wiles and tainted lures, we now crave only good.
We're cleansed from sin through Christ, our Lord; our lives have
been renewed."

Glad shouts of praise rang through the land, and solemn vows
were made
To take the Master's name that day, rememb'ring what He paid,
And lastingly revere His name, revere His fond decree—
With gratitude accept His grace, and evermore be free.

14. King Benjamin

Mosiah 3–5

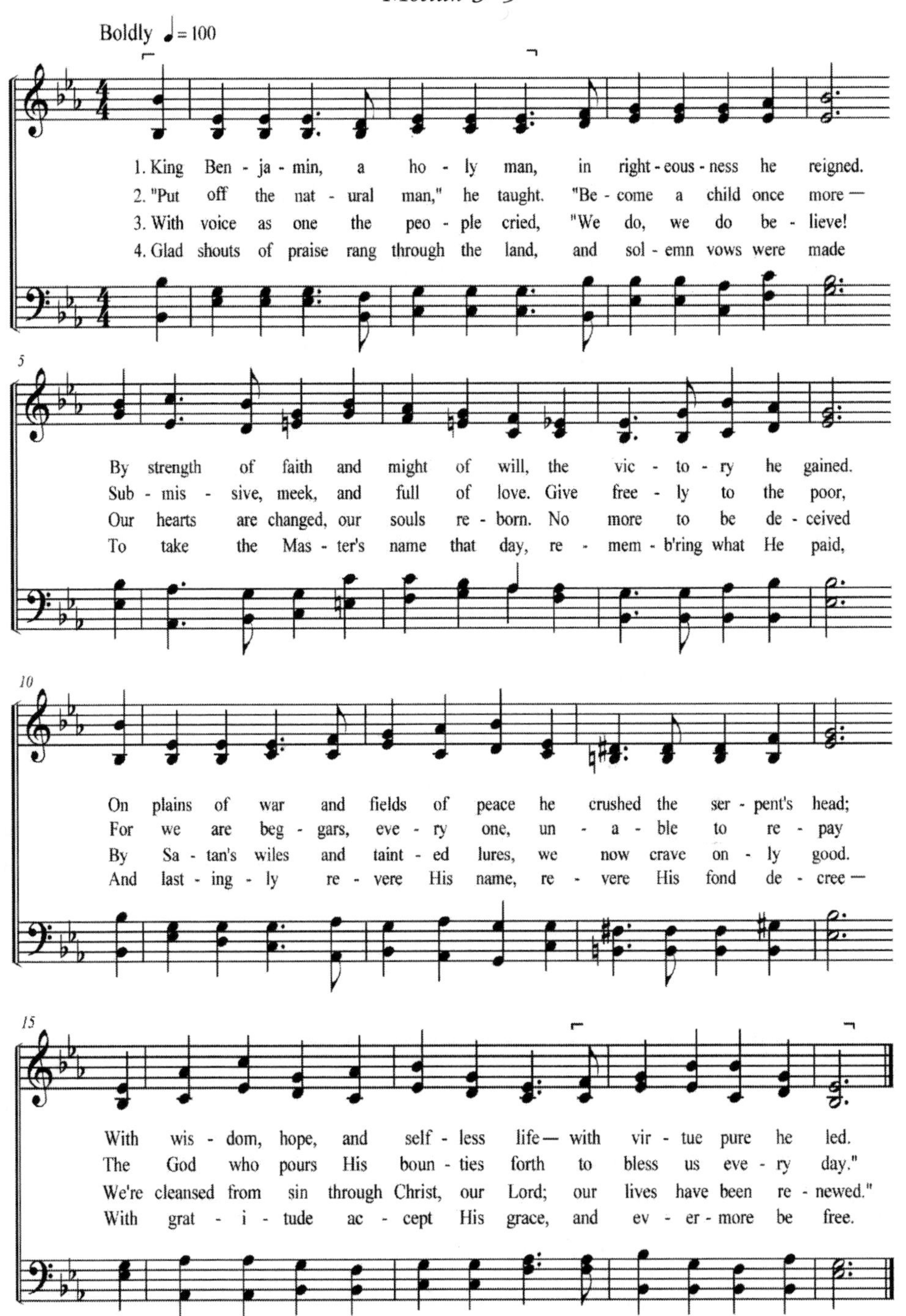
Boldly ♩ = 100
1. King Ben - ja - min, a ho - ly man, in right - eous - ness he reigned.
2. "Put off the nat - ural man," he taught. "Be - come a child once more —
3. With voice as one the peo - ple cried, "We do, we do be - lieve!
4. Glad shouts of praise rang through the land, and sol - emn vows were made
5
By strength of faith and might of will, the vic - to - ry he gained.
Sub - mis - sive, meek, and full of love. Give free - ly to the poor,
Our hearts are changed, our souls re - born. No more to be de - ceived
To take the Mas - ter's name that day, re - mem - b'ring what He paid,
10
On plains of war and fields of peace he crushed the ser - pent's head;
For we are beg - gars, eve - ry one, un - a - ble to re - pay
By Sa - tan's wiles and taint - ed lures, we now crave on - ly good.
And last - ing - ly re - vere His name, re - vere His fond de - cree —
15
With wis - dom, hope, and self - less life — with vir - tue pure he led.
The God who pours His boun - ties forth to bless us eve - ry day."
We're cleansed from sin through Christ, our Lord; our lives have been re - newed."
With grat - i - tude ac - cept His grace, and ev - er - more be free.

Text: Marilyn Arnold

Music: Maurine B. Ozment

15. The Title of Liberty

Alma 46

The title of liberty Moroni raised high and called for the brave and the strong
To fight for their freedom to worship in peace, the freedom they cherished so long.
His coat bore the words of his rallying cry, "Our God, our religion, our peace—
Our freedoms, our wives, and our children defend, and ever our honor increase."

Then donning his shields and his armor and plates, he bowed to the earth and he prayed
With might and with faith to the Great God above that freedom they'd never betray.
Proclaiming the land as a bastion of hope, a land held in trust for the free,
Moroni strode forth with his banner unfurled to shout far and wide his decree.

"Come forth in the strength of the Lord," he did cry. "Come forth, do not falter or faint.
Forsake not your God, nor your freedom and homes; find courage befitting a saint."
They answered the call and their clothing they rent; they answered his soul-stirring cry.
From towers, from roofs all across that broad land, the title leaped up to the sky.

15. The Title of Liberty

Alma 46

Boldly ♩ = 76
1. The ti - tle of li - ber - ty Mo - ro - ni raised high and called for the brave and the strong To fight for their free - dom to wor - ship in peace, the free - dom they cher - ished so long.
2. Then don - ning his shields and his ar - mor and plates, he bowed to the earth and he prayed With might and with faith to the Great God a - bove that free - dom they'd nev - er be - tray.
3. "Come forth in the strength of the Lord," he did cry. "Come forth, do not fal - ter or faint. For - sake not your God, nor your free - dom and homes; find cour - age be - fit - ting a saint."
3
6

Text: Marilyn Arnold

Music: Maurine B. Ozment

The Title of Liberty

9
His coat bore the words of his ral - ly - ing cry,
Pro - claim - ing the land as a bas - tion of hope,
They an - swered the call and their cloth - ing they rent;
12
"Our God, our re - li - gion, our peace— Our free - doms, our wives, and our
a land held in trust for the free, Mo - ro - ni strode forth with his
they an - swered his soul - stir - ring cry. From tow - ers, from roofs all a-
17
chil - dren de - fend, and ev - er our hon - or in - crease."
ban - ner un - furled to shout far and wide his de - cree.
cross that broad land, the ti - tle leaped up to the sky.

Text: Marilyn Arnold

Music: Maurine B. Ozment

16. My Little Band

(Helaman to His Stripling Warriors)
Alma 56–58

My little band, my sons, my sons, will ye to battle go?
Will you fight fiercely for the right against our ruthless foe?
What say ye, sons, so young and pure, will you coarse weapons wield?
Will you fight bravely at my side, with virtue as your shield?

Young warriors respond:

Yes, yes, our father, we will fight,
For truth our all we'll give.
Our mothers' faith has vanquished fright;
They said, doubt not and live.

Yes, yes, we're young, but ne'er forget
That we are firm of mind.
We'll stay the course our mothers set
With faith in God's design.

The battle's done, my little band, with strength divine you fought
Emboldened by your mothers' words, by words your mothers taught.
You knew, as they, that trust in God would save each precious son,
And so it has, not one was slain. Your faith the victory won.

16. My Little Band

(Helaman to His Stripling Warriors)

Alma 56–58

With conviction ♩ = 76

Helaman speaks:

1. My lit - tle band, my sons, my sons, will ye to bat - tle go?

8
Will you fight fierce - ly for the right a - gainst our ruth - less foe?

15
What say ye, sons, so young and pure, will you coarse weap-ons wield?

Text: Marilyn Arnold

Music: Maurine B. Ozment

My Little Band

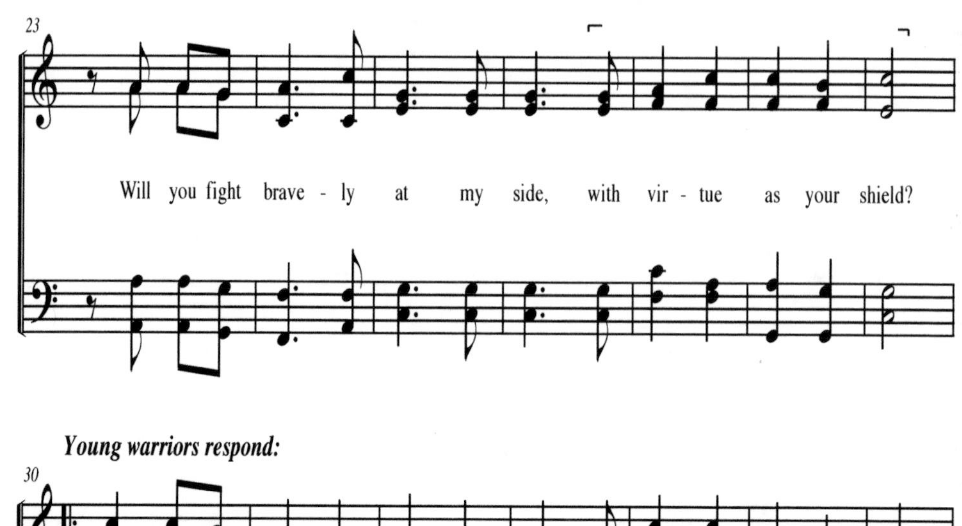

23
Will you fight brave - ly at my side, with vir - tue as your shield?

Young warriors respond:

30
2. Yes, yes, our fa - ther, we will fight, For truth our all we'll give.
3. Yes, yes, we're young, but ne'er for - get That we are firm of mind.

37
Our moth - ers' faith has van - quished fright; They said, doubt not and live.
We'll stay the course our moth - ers set With faith in God's de - sign.

Text: Marilyn Arnold

Music: Maurine B. Ozment

My Little Band

Helaman speaks:
44
4. The bat - tle's done, my lit - tle band, with strength di - vine you fought
51
Em - bold - ened by your moth - ers' words, by words your moth - ers taught.
58
You knew, as they, that trust in God would save each pre - cious son,
66
And so it has, not one was slain. Your faith the vic - tory won.

Text: Marilyn Arnold

Music: Maurine B. Ozment

17. Touch These Stones

(The Brother of Jared Entreats the Lord)
Ether 3:1–16

"Touch these stones, Holy Lord—give us light, give us light
for our journey across many seas.
Touch these stones with Thy hand—let them shine, let them shine;
Blessed Lord, hear and answer my plea."

Refrain

Such faith had the brother of Jared that day
That the Lord withheld naught from his gaze.
A man saw God's finger igniting each stone
And then, O then, looked on His face!

"Touch these stones, Mighty Lord, turn Thine anger away;
all our follies we beg Thee forgive.
We are weak, Thou art strong, grant us power from Thy hand.
Let us travel in light, let us live!"

"Touch these stones, Precious Lord, that our ships may have light,"
was the prayer that unlocked golden doors.
"Touch these stones," voiced in faith summoned heaven to earth,
where a man saw himself in his Lord.

17. Touch These Stones

(The Brother of Jared Entreats the Lord)

Ether 3:1–16

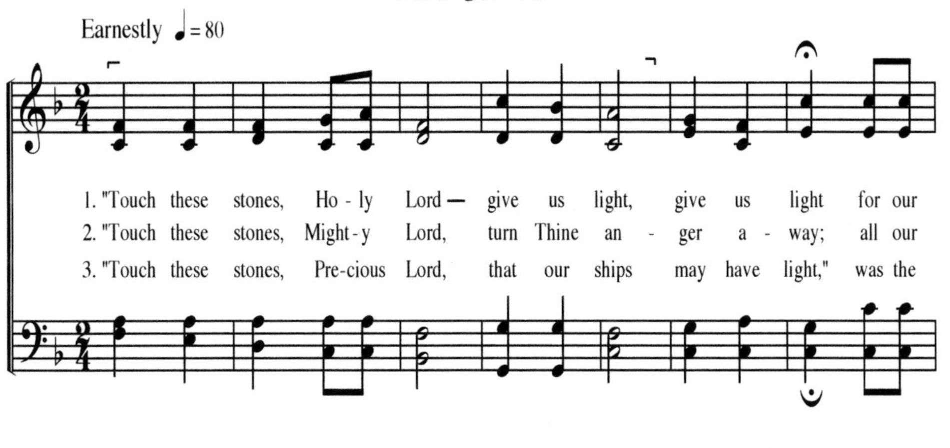
Earnestly ♩ = 80
1. "Touch these stones, Ho - ly Lord— give us light, give us light for our
2. "Touch these stones, Might-y Lord, turn Thine an - ger a - way; all our
3. "Touch these stones, Pre-cious Lord, that our ships may have light," was the

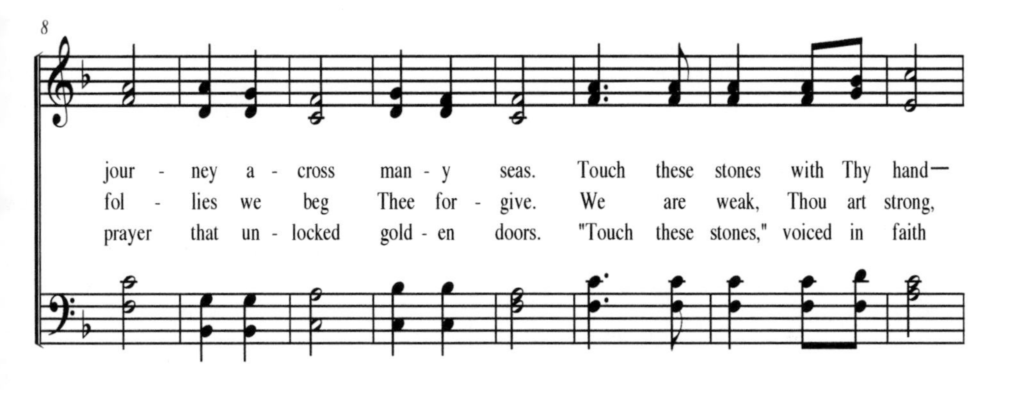
8
jour - ney a - cross man - y seas. Touch these stones with Thy hand—
fol - lies we beg Thee for - give. We are weak, Thou art strong,
prayer that un - locked gold - en doors. "Touch these stones," voiced in faith

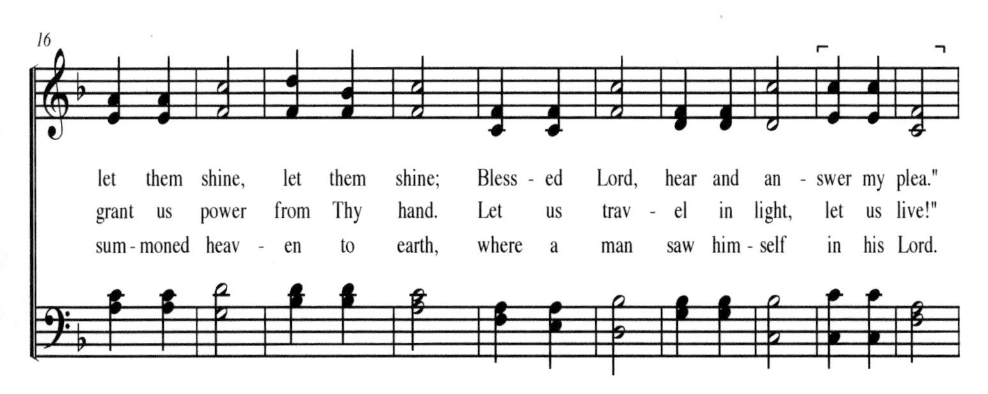
16
let them shine, let them shine; Bless - ed Lord, hear and an - swer my plea."
grant us power from Thy hand. Let us trav - el in light, let us live!"
sum-moned heav - en to earth, where a man saw him - self in his Lord.

Text: Marilyn Arnold

Music: Maurine B. Ozment

Touch These Stones

26
Refrain
Such faith had the broth - er of Jar - ed that day That the Lord with - held naught from his
33
gaze. A man saw God's fin - ger ig - nit - ing each stone And then, O then, looked on His face!

Text: Marilyn Arnold

Music: Maurine B. Ozment

18. Nephi's Vision of the Tree of Life

1 Nephi 11

I looked and I beheld a tree, a wondrous tree, so precious, rare,
with fruit delicious, mild.
An angel knew what I beheld when vision showed my wond'ring gaze
a virgin fair with child.
"Behold the Lamb of God," he said. "Behold the Lamb of God!"

The love of God, it sheds abroad like tree and living waters, fresh—
like waters pure, and free.
"Most joyous to the soul, this love," the angel cried, and well I knew
this love divine for me.
The Great Redeemer then I saw, the Great Redeemer saw.

I watched the Son of God go forth, to heal and bless the sick and lame,
the lame and sick embrace.
But proud men cast aside His love, and judged and nailed Him
to the cross, where none could take His place.
The Great Redeemer died for us, He died for love of us.

18. Nephi's Vision of the Tree of Life

1 Nephi 11
Joyfully ♩ = 66
1. I looked and I be - held a tree, a won - drous tree, so
2. The love of God, it sheds a - broad like tree and liv - ing
3. I watched the Son of God go forth, to heal and bless the
7
pre - cious, rare, with fruit de - li - cious, mild. An an - gel
wa - ters, fresh— like wa - ters pure, and free. "Most joy - ous
sick and lame, the lame and sick em - brace. But proud men
14
knew what I be - held when vi - sion showed my won - d'ring
to the soul, this love," the an - gel cried, and well I
cast a - side His love, and judged and nailed Him to the

Text: Marilyn Arnold

Music: Maurine B. Ozment

Nephi's Vision of the Tree of Life

19
gaze a vir - gin fair with child. "Be - hold the Lamb of
knew this love di - vine for me. The Great Re - deem - er
cross, where none could take His place. The Great Re - deem - er

26
God," he said, "Be - hold the Lamb of God!"
then I saw, the Great Re - deem - er saw.
died for us, He died for love of us.

Text: Marilyn Arnold

Music: Maurine B. Ozment

19. Surrounded by Fire

(Helaman's Sons Witness a Miracle)
Helaman 5

Introductory and concluding refrain

"Remember, remember," their father had said,
"Remember our fathers now gone.
Remember, remember their teachings of Him
Who came to redeem and atone."

Surrounded by fire, and yet spared from the flames, in prison the brothers stood forth;
Surrounded by fire, then enveloped in cloud, while God's mighty power shook the earth.
Then twice came a voice—piercing, soft—from the dark, "Repent ye, the Kingdom's at hand."
Once more spoke the voice to the wondering crowd, in language beyond speech of man.

The Lamanites cried to the whispering voice; each soul was encircled with fire.
The Spirit of God filled their hearts, filled their hearts; the cloud was dispersed by desire.
"Peace, peace unto you," said the whispering voice. "Know peace through your faith in My Son."
Those three hundred souls went abroad then to teach, and thousands joined with them as one.

19. Surrounded by Fire

(Helaman's Sons Witness a Miracle)

Helaman 5

Fervently ♩ = 66
Introductory refrain
"Re - mem-ber, re - mem-ber," their fa - ther had said, "Re - mem - ber our
fa - thers now gone. Re - mem - ber, re - mem - ber their teach - ings of Him Who
came to re - deem and a - tone."
1. Sur - round - ed by fire, and yet
2. The La - man - ites cried to the
spared from the flames, in pris - on the broth - ers stood forth;
whis - per - ing voice; each soul was en - cir - cled with fire.

Text: Marilyn Arnold

Music: Maurine B. Ozment

Surrounded by Fire

23
Sur - round - ed by fire, then en - vel - oped in cloud, while God's might - y
The Spir - it of God filled their hearts, filled their hearts; the cloud was dis-
29
power shook the earth. Then twice came a voice — pierc - ing, soft — from the
persed by de - sire. "Peace, peace un - to you," said the whis - per - ing
34
dark, "Re - pent ye, the King - dom's at hand." Once more spoke the
voice, "Know peace through your faith in My Son." Those three hun - dred
39
voice to the won - der - ing crowd, in lan - guage be - yond speech of man.
souls went a - broad then to teach, and thou - sands joined with them as one.
(To Concluding Refrain)

Text: Marilyn Arnold

Music: Maurine B. Ozment

Surrounded by Fire

45
Concluding refrain
"Re - mem - ber, re - mem - ber," their fa - ther had said, "Re-

50
mem - ber our fa - thers now gone. Re - mem - ber, re - mem - ber their

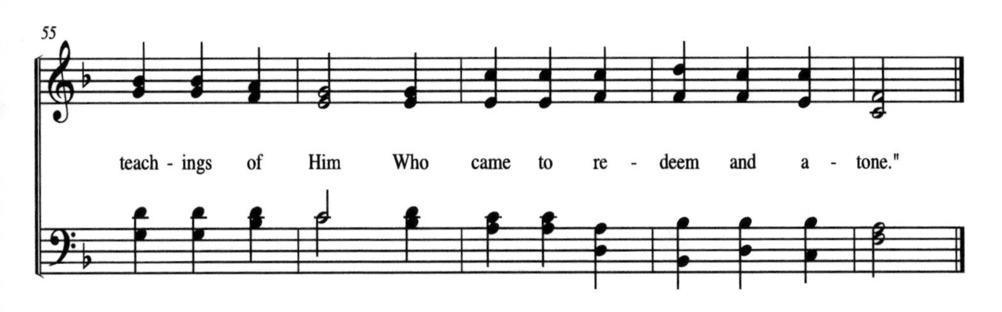
55
teach - ings of Him Who came to re - deem and a - tone."

Text: Marilyn Arnold

Music: Maurine B. Ozment

20. Then He Comes, Then He Comes

(Samuel the Lamanite Prophesies of the Savior)
Helaman 14

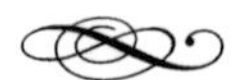

"Five years will pass by, then He comes, then He comes,
the Son of God comes, our Redeemer."
So cried Samuel out from the top of the wall
to the Nephites, who thought him a dreamer.

Refrain

Imagine him there, dauntless Samuel of old,
For crying repentance they scorned him.
Imagine him dodging their arrows and stones,
His arm reaching forth as he warned them.

"You'll see when He comes, you will see, you will see,
great lights in the heavens surrounding.
'Twill seem like one day, for no darkness will fall
for two days and a night, all confounding."

"When signs fill the earth, you will know, you will know
our Lord will be born at the dawning;
A star will appear for the first time that night,
full of splendor and bright as the morning."

20. Then He Comes, Then He Comes (cont.)

Interlude (change of tone)

The signs of his birth are all glorious and bright,
But when He is slain, it is dark as the night.
For three days it's dark as the night.
Great rocks split apart and are scattered afar,
No light for three days, not from sun, moon, or star,
For three days, no sun, moon, or star.

"Remember, remember, you're free to believe.
Remember," cried Samuel, "your choice is
For life or for death. Ye are free, ye are free—
whoso chooses His path then rejoices."

20. Then He Comes, Then He Comes

(Samuel the Lamanite Prophesies of the Savior)

Helaman 14

Fervently ♩= 72
1. "Five years will pass by, then He comes, then He comes, The Son of God comes, our Re - deem - er." So cried Sam - uel out from the top of the wall To the Ne - phites, who thought him a dream - er.
2. "You'll see when He comes, you will see, you will see, Great lights in the heav - ens sur - round - ing. 'Twill seem like one day, for no dark - ness will fall For two days and a night, all con- found - ing."
3. "When signs fill the earth, you will know, you will know Our Lord will be born at the dawn - ing; A star will ap - pear for the first time that night, Full of splen - dor and bright as the morn - ing."
Refrain ♩= 88
Im - ag - ine him there, daunt - less Sam - uel of old, For

Text: Marilyn Arnold

Music: Maurine B. Ozment

Then He Comes, Then He Comes

15
cry - ing re - pent - ance they scorned him. Im - ag - ine him dodg - ing their ar - rows and
21
Interlude (after verse 3)
stones, His arm reach - ing forth as he warned them. The signs of His birth are all
29
glo - rious and bright, But when He is slain, it is dark as the night.
35
For three days it's dark as the night. Great rocks split a - part and are scat-tered a-

Text: Marilyn Arnold

Music: Maurine B. Ozment

Then He Comes, Then He Comes

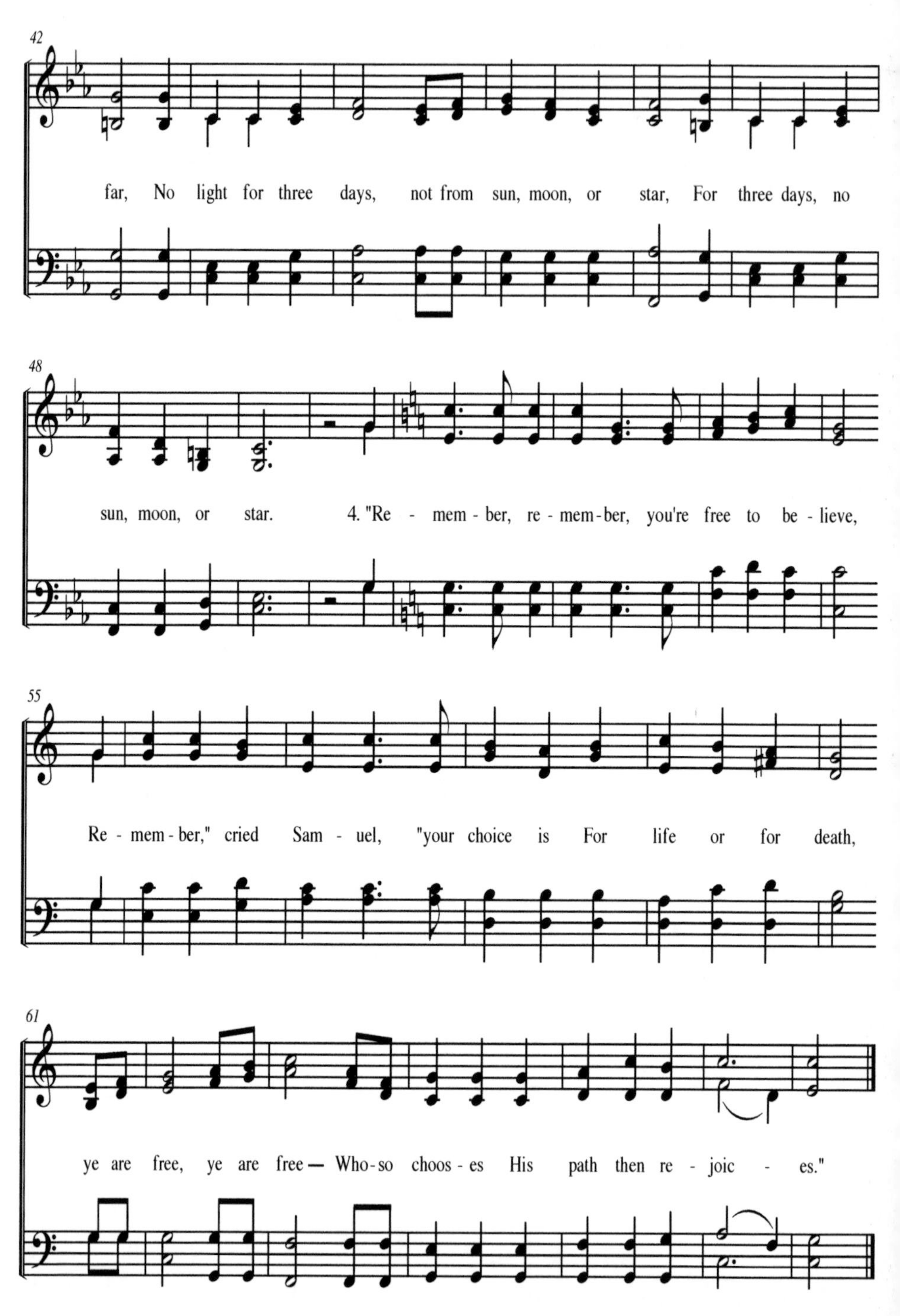
42
far, No light for three days, not from sun, moon, or star, For three days, no
48
sun, moon, or star. 4. "Re - mem - ber, re - mem - ber, you're free to be - lieve,
55
Re - mem - ber," cried Sam - uel, "your choice is For life or for death,
61
ye are free, ye are free — Who - so choos - es His path then re - joic - es."

Text: Marilyn Arnold

Music: Maurine B. Ozment

21. The Time Is at Hand

(The Lord Announces His Coming)
3 Nephi 1

"Lift up your head and be of good cheer, for behold, the time is at hand;
This night shall the sign you have watched for so long be manifest over
the land."
So spoke the Lord God from heaven above as Nephi beseeched Him
in prayer;
He cried all that day, seeking God's holy aid, the lives of the faithful
to spare.

Refrain

"The prophets foretold I would come, I would come,
And now is the hour of my birth,
The hour when the King of Creation descends
To save all the children of earth."

"Lift up your head, fear nothing my son, for behold, the signs
are unfurled.
This night will the skies render witness that I tomorrow am born
to the world."
Yea, just as He said, no darkness befell, the night was as bright as
the morn;
And every soul knew that at last it had come, the day that the
Christ would be born.

21. The Time Is at Hand

(The Lord Announces His Coming)

3 Nephi 1

Joyfully ♩ = 104

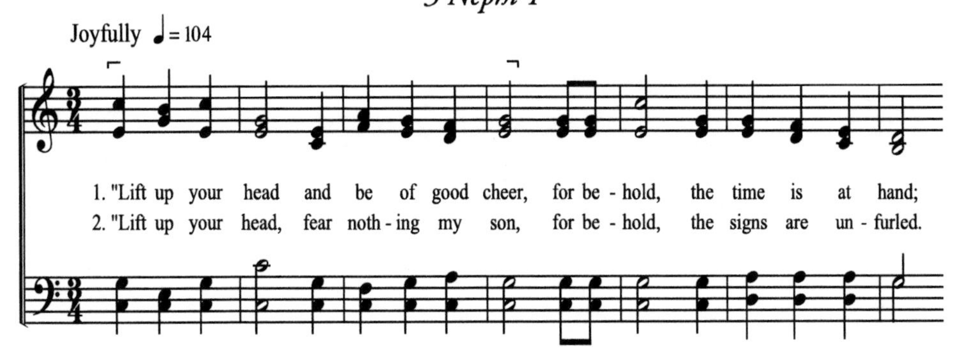

1. "Lift up your head and be of good cheer, for be - hold, the time is at hand;
2. "Lift up your head, fear noth - ing my son, for be - hold, the signs are un - furled.

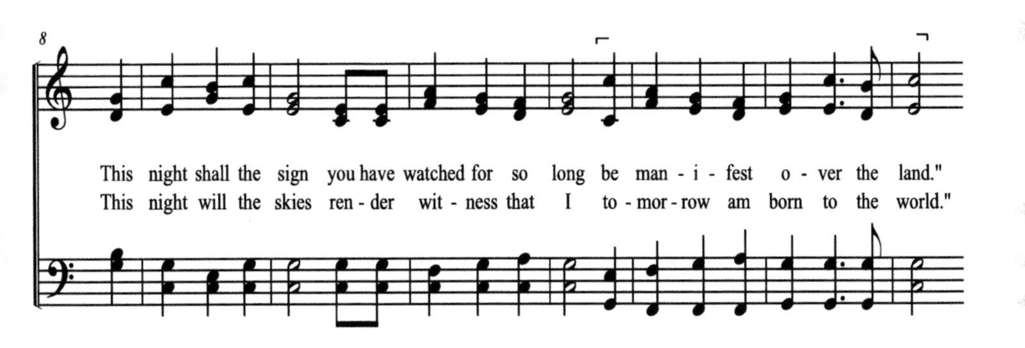

8
This night shall the sign you have watched for so long be man - i - fest o - ver the land."
This night will the skies ren - der wit - ness that I to - mor - row am born to the world."

16
So spoke the Lord God from heav - en a - bove as Ne - phi be - seeched Him in prayer;
Yea, just as He said, no dark-ness be - fell, the night was as bright as the morn;

Text: Marilyn Arnold

Music: Maurine B. Ozment

The Time Is at Hand

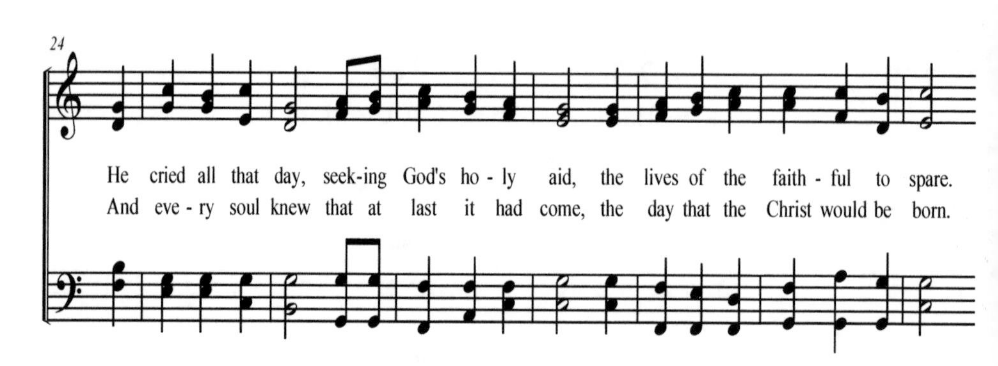
24
He cried all that day, seek-ing God's ho - ly aid, the lives of the faith - ful to spare.
And eve - ry soul knew that at last it had come, the day that the Christ would be born.

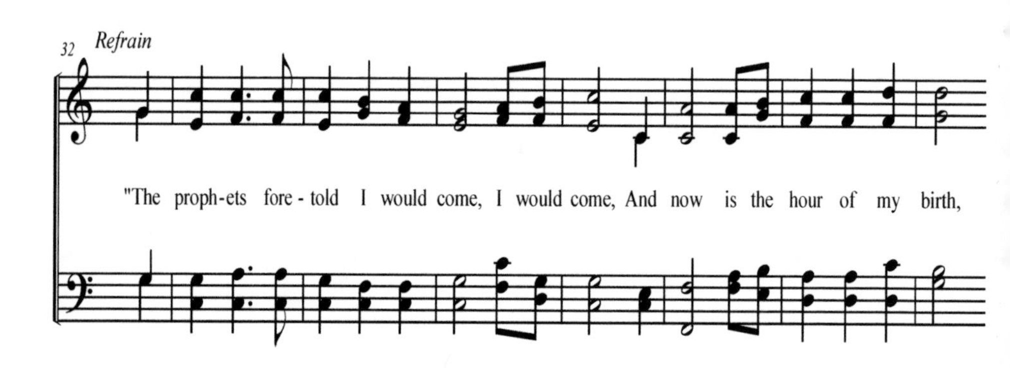
32 Refrain
"The proph-ets fore - told I would come, I would come, And now is the hour of my birth,

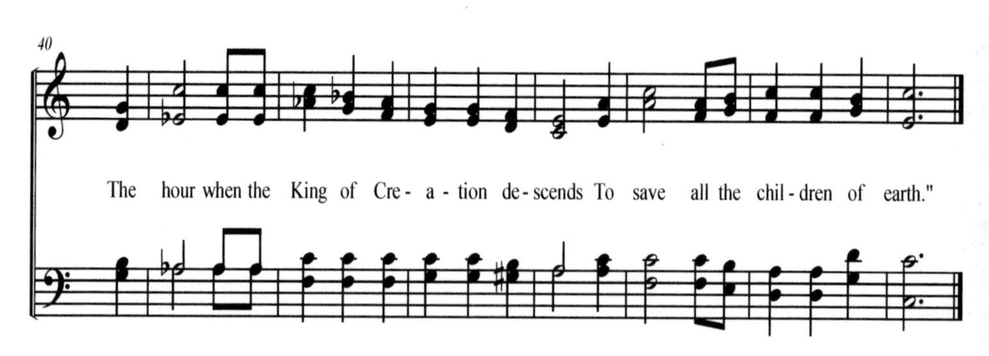
40
The hour when the King of Cre- a - tion de - scends To save all the chil - dren of earth."

Text: Marilyn Arnold

Music: Maurine B. Ozment

22. How Oft I Have Gathered You

(Christ Comforts the Desolate)
3 Nephi 8–11

As Samuel foretold, at the death of the Lord,
 wild tempests shook earth to the core.
The ground split apart, great rocks tumbled down,
 dark vapors engulfed rich and poor.
And then in the midst of the turmoil and grief,
 a voice sounded out of the night:
"Return now to me, return and be healed.
 Christ, Jesus, I am, bringing light."

Refrain

How oft I have gathered you, as a hen doth her young,
But how oft you would not, you would not.
Yet still I will gather you, Israel mine, ever mine,
'Neath my wings, then no more you will not.

Three days passed away, and the tumult did cease;
 dark mist fled the face of the land.
A voice, oh so still, pierced hearts with these words,
 "Behold, now my Son is at hand."
Eyes upward were cast where a Man all in white
 descended as throngs fell in awe.
"Arise and come forth," thus He beckoned to them.
 "I'm He, whom the prophets foresaw."

22. How Oft I Have Gathered You

(Christ Comforts the Desolate)

3 Nephi 8–11

Fervently ♩ = 72
Unison
1. As Sam - uel fore - told, at the death of the Lord, wild tem - pests shook earth to the core. The ground split a - part, great rocks tum - bled down, dark va - pors en - gulfed rich and poor.
2. Three days passed a - way, and the tu - mult did cease; dark mist fled the face of the land. A voice, oh so still, pierced hearts with these words, "Be - hold, now my Son is at hand."
3
6

Text: Marilyn Arnold

Music: Maurine B. Ozment

How Oft I Have Gathered You

9
And then in the midst of the tur - moil and grief, a
Eyes up - ward were cast where a Man all in white de-
12
voice sound - ed out of the night: "Re - turn now to me, re-
scend - ed as throngs fell in awe. "A - rise and come forth," thus He
15
turn and be healed. Christ, Je - sus, I am, bring - ing light."
beck - oned to them, "I'm He, whom the proph - ets fore - saw."

Text: Marilyn Arnold

Music: Maurine B. Ozment

How Oft I Have Gathered You

19
Refrain
Harmony
How oft I have gath - ered you, as a hen doth her
Optional
accompaniment

22
young, But how oft you would not,

Text: Marilyn Arnold

Music: Maurine B. Ozment

How Oft I Have Gathered You

25
you would not. Yet still I will gath - er you,

28
Is - rael mine, ev - er mine,

Text: Marilyn Arnold

Music: Maurine B. Ozment

How Oft I Have Gathered You

30
'Neath my wings, then no more
32
1.
2.
you will not.
not.

Text: Marilyn Arnold

Music: Maurine B. Ozment

23. Things Old Are Done Away

(Christ Speaks to the Surviving Nephites)
3 Nephi 11, 15

"Things old are done, are done away;
in me, all things are new.
Come, feel the prints in hands and feet
where nails once pierced me through.

"Behold, I'm Christ, the One foretold,
I've drunk the bitter cup.
Beloved, your sins I bore for you,
for you was lifted up.

"I'm Jesus Christ who prophets said
would come to save and heal.
I'm Jesus Christ, your light and life,
I do the Father's will."

So spoke our Lord that bright new day
to souls once wracked with fear;
So spoke our Lord when he came down
and blessed His people here.

He lifted us and gave us hope,
we worshiped and adored.
He taught us love—sing praise, sing praise—
Hosanna! Most High God!

23. Things Old Are Done Away

(Christ Speaks to the Surviving Nephites)

3 Nephi 11, 15

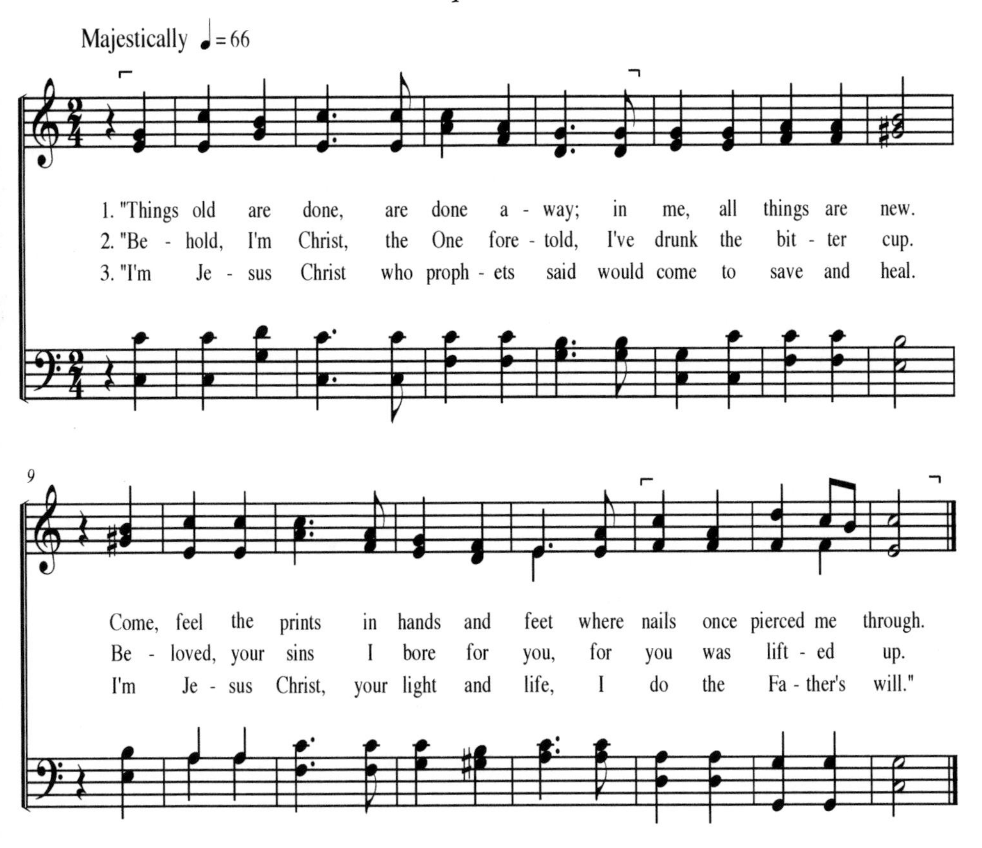

Majestically ♩ = 66
1. "Things old are done, are done a - way; in me, all things are new.
2. "Be - hold, I'm Christ, the One fore - told, I've drunk the bit - ter cup.
3. "I'm Je - sus Christ who proph - ets said would come to save and heal.
9
Come, feel the prints in hands and feet where nails once pierced me through.
Be - loved, your sins I bore for you, for you was lift - ed up.
I'm Je - sus Christ, your light and life, I do the Fa - ther's will."

4. So spoke our Lord that bright new day
   To souls once wracked with fear;
   So spoke our Lord when He came down
   And blessed His people here.

5. He lifted us and gave us hope,
   We worshipped and adored.
   He taught us love—sing praise, sing praise—
   Hosanna! Most High God!

Text: Marilyn Arnold

Music: Maurine B. Ozment

24. Come, Come, My Child

(Jesus Blesses the Nephite Children)
3 Nephi 17

Come, come, my child, and I will tell the story that you love so well,
How Jesus came, God's Holy Son, and blessed the children one by one
As 'round His feet they gathered there, with heads bowed low to hear His prayer.
They saw Him weep for joy and love, and when they raised their eyes above,
Down angels came in bursts of light, fire transcendent, circling bright.

Please, Mother, say how you can know this thing that happened long ago.
Why did He come, why did He stay? Did all the children hear Him pray?

Yes, yes, my child, indeed they heard, and marveled long at every word;
None there could write what Jesus said, such wondrous words could not be read.

Were they afraid with fire so near, or did the angels calm their fear?
Would I have run, racing to hide? Would I have, trembling, left His side?

24. Come, Come, My Child (cont.)

No, no, my child, you would have felt His peace and love as there
you knelt.
You would have smiled and danced and sung, forgotten fear and
pain, and clung
To robe and feet with tears made wet, and never, ever, ever forget
His eyes, His hands, His touch, His voice, and in rememb'ring,
you'd rejoice.
His eyes, His hands, His touch, His voice, we'll remember Him,
we'll rejoice!

24. Come, Come, My Child

(Jesus Blesses the Nephite Children)

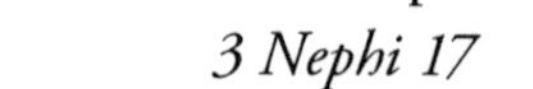

3 Nephi 17

Thoughtfully ♩=69
Mother*
1. Come, come, my child, and I will tell the sto - ry that you love so well,
4
How Je - sus came, God's Hol - y Son, and blessed the chil - dren one by one
7
As 'round His feet they gath - ered there, with heads bowed low to hear His prayer.
12
They saw Him weep for joy and love, and when they raised their eyes a - bove,

Alternate words: *Father, grandma, grandpa, teacher*

Text: Marilyn Arnold

Music: Maurine B. Ozment

Come, Come, My Child

15
Down an - gels came in bursts of light, fire tran - scen - dent, cir - cling bright.
20
♩=84
Child 2. Please, Moth - er,* say how you can know this thing that
Mother* 3. Yes, yes, my child, in - deed they heard, and mar - veled
Child 4. Were they a - fraid with fire so near, or did the
25
hap - pened long a - go. Why did He come, why did He
long at eve - ry word; None there could write what Je - sus
an - gels calm their fear? Would I have run, ra - cing to
31
stay? Did all the chil - dren hear Him pray?
said, such won - drous words could not be read.
hide? Would I have, trem - bling, left His side?

Text: Marilyn Arnold

Music: Maurine B. Ozment

Come, Come, My Child

36
Mother*
5. No, no, my child, you would have felt His peace and love as there you knelt.
39
You would have smiled and danced and sung, for - got - ten fear and pain, and clung
42
To robe and feet with tears made wet, and nev - er, ev - er, ev - er for - get
47
His eyes, His hands, His touch, His voice, and in re - mem - b'ring, you'd re - joice.
50
All
His eyes, His hands, His touch, His voice, we'll re - mem - ber Him, we'll re - joice.

Text: Marilyn Arnold

Music: Maurine B. Ozment

25. I Was There When He Came

3 Nephi 19

I was there when He came, my Lord Jesus, the Son.
I was there when He bid all the children to come.
I was one that He called as a witness to teach;
I was one of the Twelve that the Lord's hand did reach.
I was there when we prayed, each so filled with desire,
That the Spirit's descent lit my soul as with fire.

Heaven opened that day; we saw angels descend.
And then Jesus Himself, on His knees He did bend.
I was moved by His words that could never deceive;
Overwhelmed by His love, I will always believe.
Then we shone as He shone, all bedazzled in white;
It was Heaven on earth, all resplendent with light.

25. I Was There When He Came

3 Nephi 19

Fervently ♩= 66
1. I was there when He came, my Lord Je - sus, the Son. I was there when He bid all the
2. Heav-en o - pened that day; we saw an - gels de - scend. And then Je - sus Him-self, on His
chil - dren to come. I was one that He called as a wit - ness to teach; I was
knees He did bend. I was moved by His words that could nev - er de - ceive; O - ver-
one of the Twelve that the Lord's hand did reach. I was there when we prayed, each so
whelmed by His love, I will al - ways be - lieve. Then we shone as He shone, all be-
filled with de - sire, That the Spir - it's de - scent lit my soul as with fire.
daz - zled in white; It was Heav - en on earth, all re - splend - ent with light.

Text: Marilyn Arnold

Music: Maurine B. Ozment

26. We Three Were Caught Up

(Three Nephites Translated)
3 Nephi 28

We three were caught up into heaven that day,
we three who so humbly desired
To stay on the earth and bring souls unto God,
to labor, divinely inspired.

Refrain
How marvelous, how marvelous, are His works, are His works—
How marvelous God's works, and eternal.
How blessed are we to remain and to serve,
Until Jesus returns, King supernal.

"You'll not taste of death," Jesus promised us then,
"and Satan can't tempt or give pain.
The power of angels you hold in your hands,
and wondrous your works among men."

Beyond mortal harm, still we grieved over sin;
no prison nor pit held us fast.
We played with wild beasts as a child does a lamb,
when into the den we were cast.

Transformed were we three in that moment sublime
when heaven's expanse opened wide.
Unspeakable things we both heard and beheld,
beyond mortal speech to describe.

26. We Three Were Caught Up

(Three Nephites Translated)

3 Nephi 28

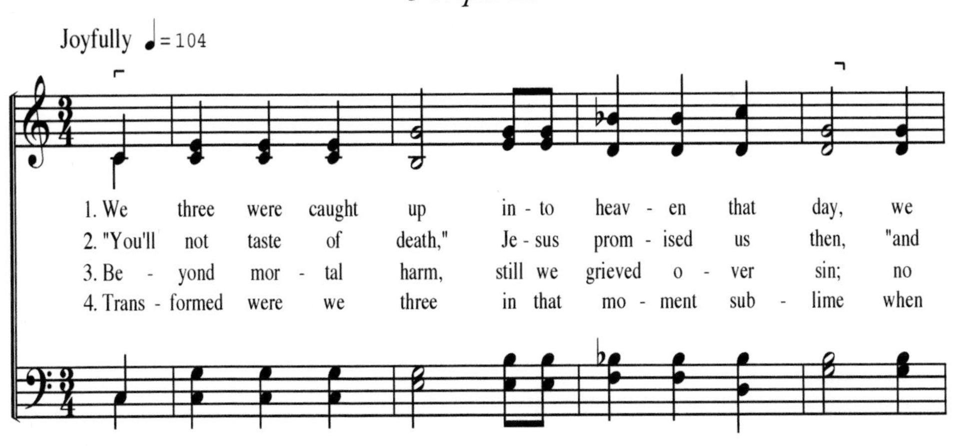

Joyfully ♩= 104
1. We three were caught up in - to heav - en that day, we
2. "You'll not taste of death," Je - sus prom - ised us then, "and
3. Be - yond mor - tal harm, still we grieved o - ver sin; no
4. Trans - formed were we three in that mo - ment sub - lime when

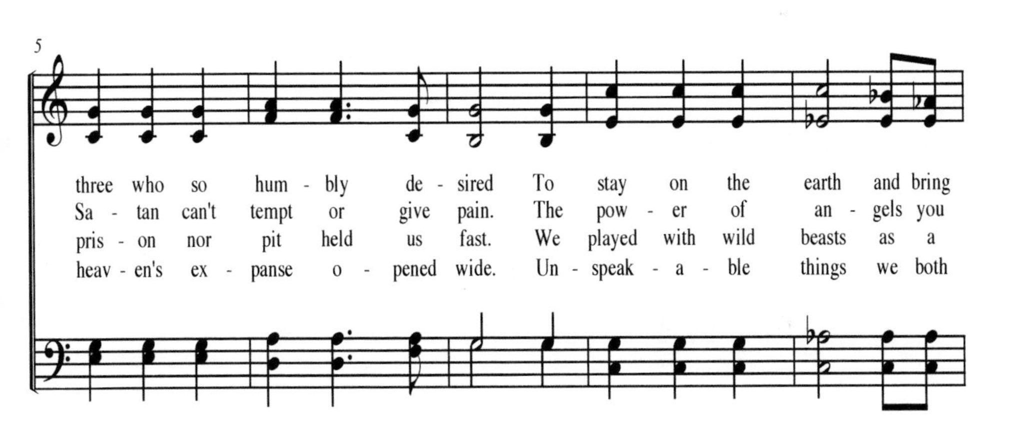

5
three who so hum - bly de - sired To stay on the earth and bring
Sa - tan can't tempt or give pain. The pow - er of an - gels you
pris - on nor pit held us fast. We played with wild beasts as a
heav - en's ex - panse o - pened wide. Un - speak - a - ble things we both

10
souls un - to God, to la - bor, di - vine - ly in - spired.
hold in your hands, and won - drous your works a - mong men."
child does a lamb, when in - to the den we were cast.
heard and be - held, be - yond mor - tal speech to de - scribe.

Text: Marilyn Arnold

Music: Maurine B. Ozment

We Three Were Caught Up

Refrain
15
How mar - vel - ous, how mar - vel - ous, are His works, are His works — How
20
mar - vel - ous God's works, and e - ter - nal. How bless - ed are we to re-
26
main and to serve, Un - til Je - sus re - turns, King su - per - nal.

Text: Marilyn Arnold

Music: Maurine B. Ozment

27. The Word Is a Seed

(Alma's Sermon to the Afflicted Zoramites)
Alma 32:26–43

The word is a seed, plant it deep in your heart;
yea, desire, oh desire, to receive.
Come exercise faith, oh come cherish the word—
yea, desire, oh desire, to believe.

You'll know it is good by its growth and its light.
You will feel it enlarging your soul.
Experiment now, test the word by your faith
as you nourish and help it to grow.

The harvest abounds if you care for the tree,
if your faith, your rich soil, gives it root.
Not barren your ground, neither scorched by the sun,
yea, the word springs to life and bears fruit.

27. The Word Is a Seed

(Alma's Sermon to the Afflicted Zoramites)

Alma 32:26–43

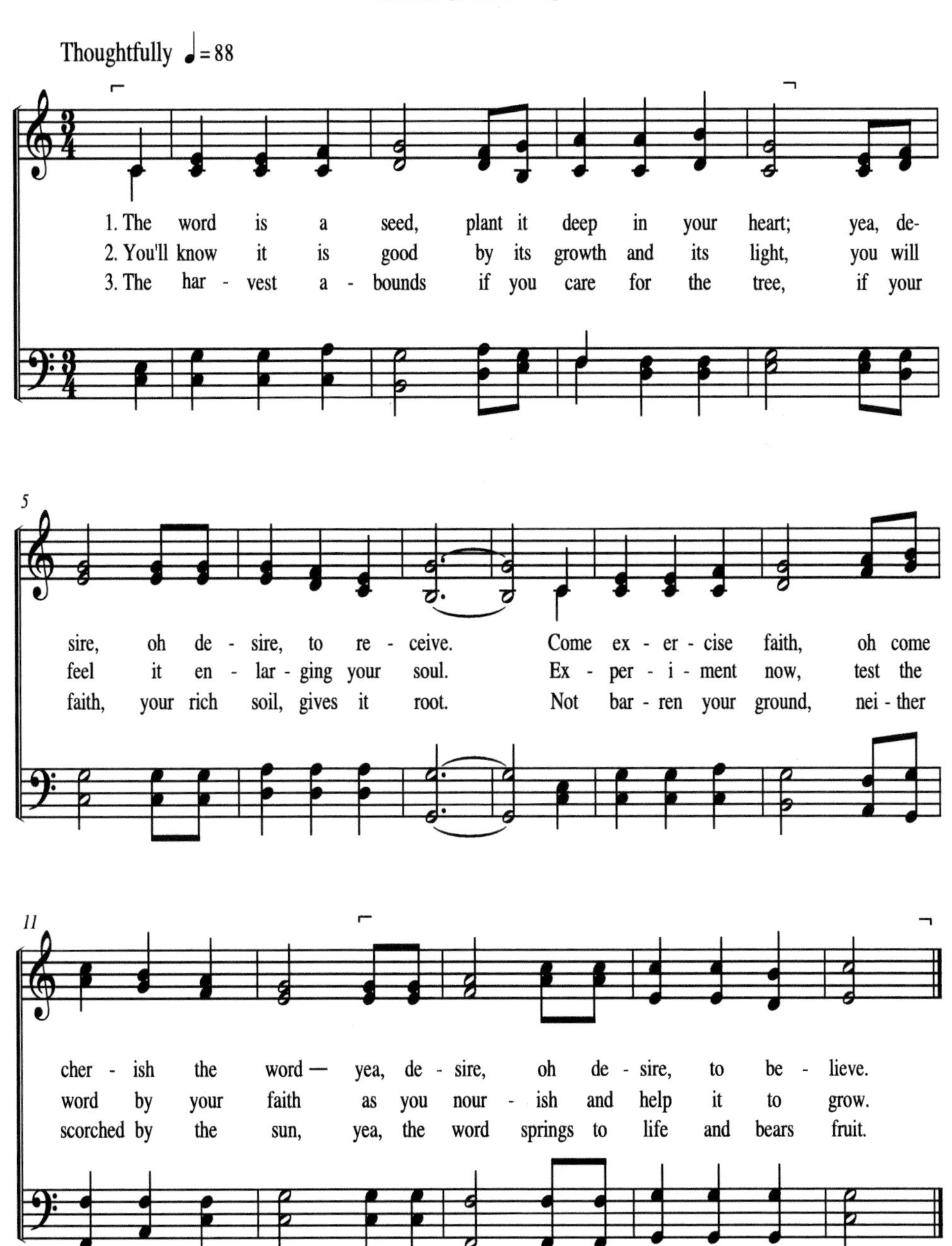

Thoughtfully ♩= 88
1. The word is a seed, plant it deep in your heart; yea, desire, oh desire, to receive. Come exercise faith, oh come cherish the word — yea, desire, oh desire, to believe.
2. You'll know it is good by its growth and its light, you will feel it enlarging your soul. Experiment now, test the word by your faith as you nourish and help it to grow.
3. The harvest abounds if you care for the tree, if your faith, your rich soil, gives it root. Not barren your ground, neither scorched by the sun, yea, the word springs to life and bears fruit.
5
11

Text: Marilyn Arnold

Music: Maurine B. Ozment

28. Cry Unto Him

(Amulek Counsels the Afflicted Zoramites)
Alma 34:17–29

Cry unto Him, yes, call His name, seek mercy at His hand,
Continue long in prayer to Him who saves without remand.
Cry unto Him in field and house, and over all that's dear;
Cry morning, midday, cry at night, and God your plea will hear.

Cry unto Him against your foes, that they won't overpower.
Against the devil also cry; forsake the evil hour.
Cry over flocks that they'll increase, and cry for mercy, too;
Cry over crops with humble heart, and God will prosper you.

Cry unto Him in secret place, repent and bare your soul
In closet and your wilderness. Let Him now make you whole.
Pray unto Him for others, too, and uttered words now prove;
Go forth to nourish burdened souls with charity and love.

28. Cry Unto Him

(Amulek Counsels the Afflicted Zoramites)

Alma 34:17–29

Earnestly ♩= 108
1. Cry un - to Him, yes, call His name, seek mer - cy at His hand,
2. Cry un - to Him a - gainst your foes, that they won't o - ver - power.
3. Cry un - to Him in se - cret place, re - pent and bare your soul
8
Con - tin - ue long in prayer to Him who saves with - out re - mand.
A - gainst the dev - il al - so cry; for - sake the e - vil hour.
In clos - et and your wil - der - ness. Let Him now make you whole.
16
Cry un - to Him in field and house, and o - ver all that's dear; Cry
Cry o - ver flocks that they'll in - crease, and cry for mer - cy, too; Cry
Pray un - to Him for oth - ers, too, and ut - tered words now prove; Go
23
morn - ing, mid - day, cry at night, and God your plea will hear.
o - ver crops with hum - ble heart, and God will pros - per you.
forth to nour - ish bur - dened souls with char - i - ty and love.

Text: Marilyn Arnold

Music: Maurine B. Ozment

29. The Lord Sheltered Ether

Ether 1:5–6; 12:1–5; 13:2–14, 18–22; 15:33–34

The Lord sheltered Ether and sent him to teach
    that repentance brings solace and peace.
But none would pay heed in that Jaredite land,
    and none their atrocities cease.

Refrain

He hid in a cave, in a shelter of rock,
He hid so the tale could be told
Of people once blessed who spurned faith in their God
And their birthright so carelessly sold.

Just who is this prophet we rarely acclaim,
    oft forgetting the price that he paid?
Just who is this prophet Moroni revered,
    whose record he tenderly saved?

He too watched his people consumed by their hate,
    and he too saw his people hewn down;
He too kept a record, he too clung to hope,
    he too would one day wear a crown.

Jerusalem New he foresaw would be built
    on a land the Lord chose of great worth.
Two cities most holy, where God's people dwell
    would herald new heaven and earth.

29. The Lord Sheltered Ether

Ether 1:5–6; 12:1–5; 13:2–14; 18–22; 15:33–34

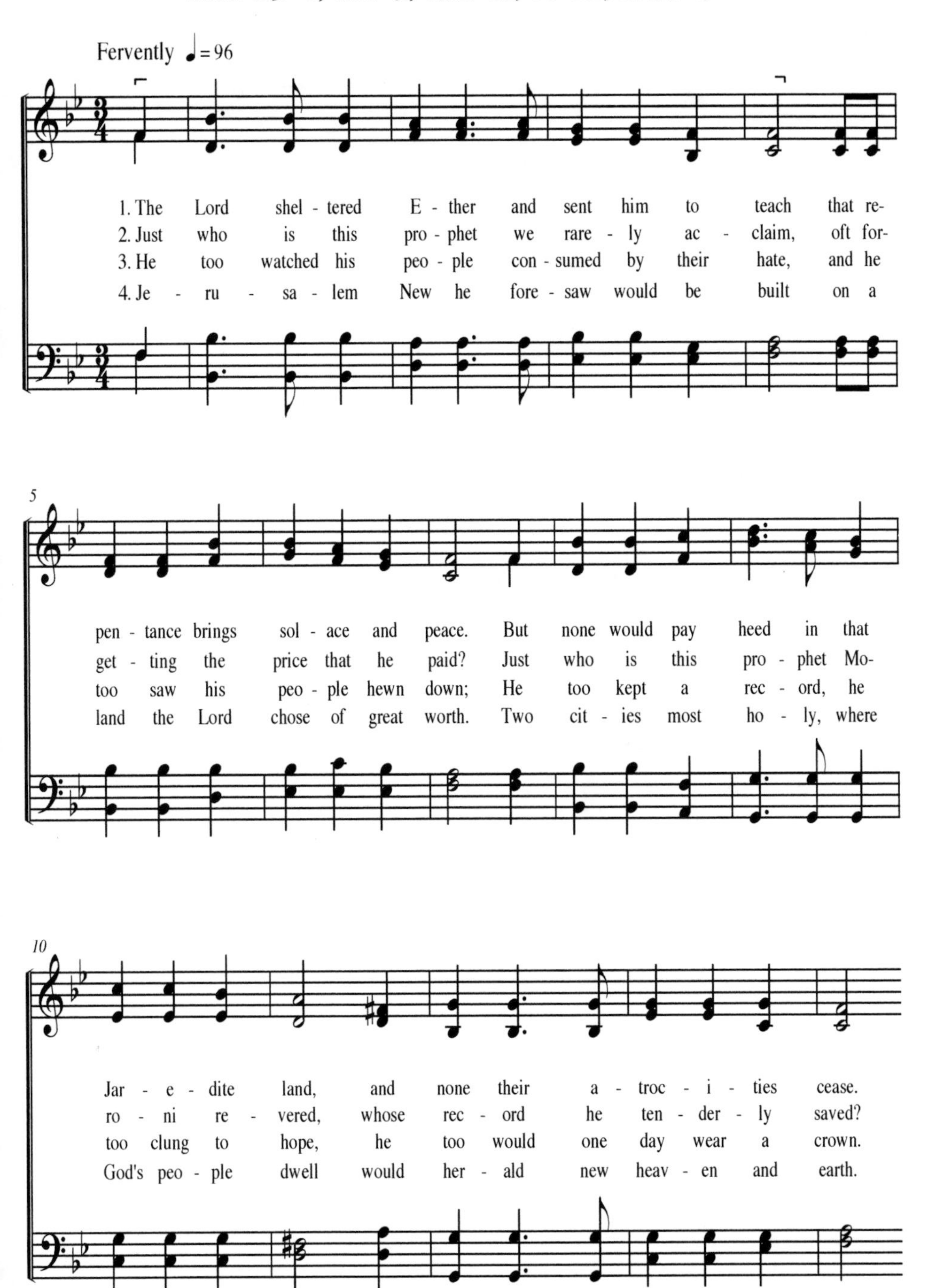

Fervently ♩ = 96
1. The Lord shel - tered E - ther and sent him to teach that re-
2. Just who is this pro - phet we rare - ly ac - claim, oft for-
3. He too watched his peo - ple con - sumed by their hate, and he
4. Je - ru - sa - lem New he fore - saw would be built on a
5
pen - tance brings sol - ace and peace. But none would pay heed in that
get - ting the price that he paid? Just who is this pro - phet Mo-
too saw his peo - ple hewn down; He too kept a rec - ord, he
land the Lord chose of great worth. Two cit - ies most ho - ly, where
10
Jar - e - dite land, and none their a - troc - i - ties cease.
ro - ni re - vered, whose rec - ord he ten - der - ly saved?
too clung to hope, he too would one day wear a crown.
God's peo - ple dwell would her - ald new heav - en and earth.

Text: Marilyn Arnold

Music: Maurine B. Ozment

The Lord Sheltered Ether

15
Refrain
He hid in a cave, in a shel-ter of rock, He hid so the tale could be told Of
23
peo-ple once blessed who spurned faith in their God And their birth-right so care-less-ly sold.

Text: Marilyn Arnold

Music: Maurine B. Ozment

30. Mormon's Lament

Mormon 6

Ten thousand strong, they fell in death, ten times ten thousand men,
Beneath Cumorah Hill hewn down, ten thousand men times ten.
When morning broke but twenty-four remained to count the cost
Of sin-filled lives and stubborn wills—the Nephite nation lost.

With heavy heart stood Mormon there, his wounds so grievous sore.
Atop Cumorah Hill he wept; his people were no more.
They lay upon the earth, all slain, their bodies bruised and torn—
None left to fight or bury dead, just twenty-four to mourn.

Then Mormon cried aloud in grief, his soul with anguish rent,
To see the carnage war had brought where once had been content.
"O fair ones mine, ye fair ones dear, how could you turn away
From Christ, our Lord, whose loving arms stretched toward you
every day?

"O fair ones mine, ye fair ones dear, fair sons and daughters gone,
One day you'll stand before His seat and all your follies own.
You willed destruction, vanquished peace, repented not from sin;
If God grants mercy to your souls, perchance we'll meet again."

30. Mormon's Lament

Mormon 6
Mournfully ♩= 72
1. Ten thou - sand strong, they fell in death, ten times ten thou - sand men,
2. With heav - y heart stood Mor - mon there, his wounds so griev - ous sore.
3. Then Mor - mon cried a - loud in grief, his soul with an - guish rent,
4. "O fair ones mine, ye fair ones dear, fair sons and daugh - ters gone,
Be - neath Cu - mor - ah Hill hewn down, ten thou - sand men times ten.
A - top Cu - mor - ah Hill he wept; his peo - ple were no more.
To see the car - nage war had brought where once had been con - tent.
One day you'll stand be - fore His seat and all your fol - lies own.
When morn - ing broke but twen - ty - four re - mained to count the cost
They lay up - on the earth, all slain, their bod - ies bruised and torn—
"O fair ones mine, ye fair ones dear, how could you turn a - way
You willed de - struc - tion, van - quished peace, re - pent - ed not from sin;
Of sin - filled lives and stub - born wills — the Ne - phite na - tion lost.
None left to fight or bur - y dead, just twen - ty - four to mourn.
From Christ, our Lord, whose lov - ing arms stretched toward you eve - ry day?
If God grants mer - cy to your souls, per - chance we'll meet a - gain."

Text: Marilyn Arnold

Music: Maurine B. Ozment

31. Ye May Know If I Write What Is True

(Moroni's Closing Exhortation)
Moroni 10

Ye may know if I write what is true, what is true;
    the Father will answer your seeking.
With a heart that's sincere, and with faith in His Son,
    ask fervently, humbly entreating.

When we meet, you and I, at the throne of our God,
    He'll point to the words I'm declaring,
Claiming all as His words, every utterance His,
    each word that I write, nothing sparing.

Therefore come unto Christ, and lay hold of his gifts;
    awake and prepare for the moment
When you stand at the bar, and I greet you with joy,
    The bar of Jehovah triumphant!

31. Ye May Know If I Write What Is True

(Moroni's Closing Exhortation)

Moroni 10

Boldly ♩= 72
1. Ye may know if I write what is true, what is true; the Fa - ther will an - swer your seek - ing. With a heart that's sin - cere, and with faith in His Son, ask fer - vent - ly, hum - bly en - treat - ing.
2. When we meet, you and I, at the throne of our God, He'll point to the words I'm de - clar - ing, Claim - ing all as His words, eve - ry ut - ter - ance His, each word that I write, noth - ing spar - ing.
3. There - fore come un - to Christ, and lay hold of His gifts; a- wake and pre - pare for the mo - ment When you stand at the bar, and I greet you with joy, the bar of Je - ho - vah tri - um - phant!

Text: Marilyn Arnold

Music: Maurine B. Ozment

32. The Book Speaks to Me

The Book of Mormon All-inclusive

A wonder foretold is entrusted to us, a book that restores truth
to man.
A marvelous work bearing witness of Christ, His gospel revealed
once again.
Absorb every page, every sentence and phrase; embrace it and hold it
most dear.
This work so sublime was prepared for our day in language both lofty
and clear.

The book speaks to me as no other has done; its stories and
teachings profound
Have altered my life, changed my heart, touched my soul—brought
joy without end, without bounds.
I read Mormon's words and I think of him there, preparing this
record for me,
Though compassed by death and atrocities dire, resolved to fulfill
God's decree.

No greater men walked on the earth than these few—the Nephis,
and Almas, and more:
Moroni, the first, rescued freedom and homes; Moroni, the last,
anguish bore.
The Lehis and Jacob, and Ammon the bold, and Samuel I'll
never forget;

32. The Book Speaks to Me (cont.)

The Lamanite kings who converted to faith—revere them and
honor them yet.

Hail Enos and Aaron and Benjamin, too; Mosiah, Abinadi, Sam.
Hail Amulek, Ether, and Helaman brave, so gentle and slow to
cast blame.
I'll read from this book every day of my life, I'll cherish the truths
it declares;
I'll thank Thee, O Lord, for the gift of Thy word, a gift beyond
price or compare.

32. The Book Speaks to Me

The Book of Mormon All-inclusive

Joyfully ♩= 112
1. A won - der fore - told is en - trust - ed to us, a
2. The book speaks to me as no oth - er has done; its
3. No great - er men walked on the earth than these few — the
4. Hail E - nos and Aar - on and Ben - ja - min, too; Mo-
book that re - stores truth to man. A mar - vel - ous
sto - ries and teach - ings pro - found Have al - tered my
Ne - phis and Al - mas, and more: Mo - ro - ni, the
si - ah, A - bin - a - di, Sam. Hail Am - u - lek,
work bear - ing wit - ness of Christ, His gos - pel re-
life, changed my heart, touched my soul — brought joy with - out
first, res - cued free - dom and homes; Mo - ro - ni, the
E - ther, and He - la - man brave, so gen - tle and
vealed once a - gain. Ab - sorb eve - ry page, eve - ry
end, with - out bounds. I read Mor - mon's words and I
last, an - guish bore. The Le - his and Ja - cob, and
slow to cast blame. I'll read from this book eve - ry

Text: Marilyn Arnold

Music: Maurine B. Ozment

The Book Speaks to Me

17
sen - tence and phrase; em - brace it and hold it most
think of him there, pre - par - ing this rec - ord for
Am - mon the bold, and Sam - uel I'll nev - er for-
day of my life, I'll cher - ish the truths it de-
21
dear. This work so sub - lime was pre - pared for our
me, Though com - passed by death and a - troc - i - ties
get; The La - man - ite kings who con - vert - ed to
clares; I'll thank Thee, O Lord, for the gift of Thy
25
day in lan - guage both lof - ty and clear.
dire, re - solved to ful - fill God's de - cree.
faith — re - vere them and hon - or them yet.
word, a gift be - yond price or com - pare.

Text: Marilyn Arnold

Music: Maurine B. Ozment

An Evening of Original Hymns Inspired by the Book of Mormon

Words by Marilyn Arnold **Music by Maurine Ozment**

Welcome:

Invocation:

Narrative: Marilyn Arnold

Program: See Reverse Side

Benediction:

Members of the Double Mixed Quartet ("Choir")

Dan Bowen
Douglas Alder
David Rogers
Fred Jackson

Tamara Rogers
Shareen Potter
Candace Potter
Kinny Stubbs

©Debbie G. Harman 1998

Program for *An Evening of Original Hymns Inspired by the Book of Mormon*
Wednesday, April 2, 2008

An Evening of Original Hymns Inspired by the Book of Mormon

April 2, 2008, 7 p.m. St. George Tabernacle

Program

"From the Dust Shall They Come" — Choir
Trumpet: Clair Reese — Accompanist: Carol Bowen

"With Hungry Soul" — Solo: Dan Bowen
Accompanist: Carol Bowen

"Nephi's Vision of the Tree of Life" — Solo: Nancy Hymas
Accompanist: Maurine Ozment

"Lehite Women" — Trio: Stacie Shurtliff, Glenna Burdick, Rebecca Lemon
Violin: Carol Sue Ettinger — Accompanist: Maurine Ozment

"Nephi's Psalm" — Choir
Accompanist: Carol Bowen

"Waters of Mormon" — Solo: Nancy Hymas
Accompanist: Lisa Farr

"Our Swords Are Made Bright" — Male Quartet: Dan Bowen, Douglas Alder, David Rogers, Fred Jackson
Solo v. 4: Dan Bowen
Accompanist: Carol Bowen

"How Oft I Have Gathered You" — Trio: Stacie Shurtliff, Glenna Burdick, Rebecca Lemmon
Accompanist: Maurine Ozment

"I Was There When He Came" — Solo: Nancy Hymas
Accompanist: Lisa Farr

"Come, Come, My Child" — Duet: Shareen Potter and Taylor Monnett
Accompanist: Lisa Farr

"Mormon's Lament" — Solo: Leon Green
Violin: Carol Sue Ettinger — Accompanist: Lisa Farr

"Receive These Words" — Choir
Accompanist: Carol Bowen

Reverse side of program for *An Evening of Original Hymns Inspired by the Book of Mormon*

THE CHURCH OF
JESUS CHRIST
OF LATTER-DAY SAINTS

ST. GEORGE UTAH TEMPLE
VISITORS' CENTER
490 South 300 East
St. George, Utah 84770-3665

April 4th, 2008

Maurine Ozment & Marilyn Arnold

Dear Maurine & Marilyn:

We were thrilled to see so many in attendance at the Tabernacle Wednesday evening. Your talents are well known and appreciated. It's a pleasure for our community to have enjoyed this program that you put so many hours into. The time Spent on this project is probably not known to many but we do know the evening was a success.

Those who participated under your direction were very good. We are aware of the countless hours you have spent composing, writing and organizing what we experienced in just an hour. Please express our gratitude to all of the artists who put their hearts, souls and voices into the production. It was an hour filled with talent and spiritual uplift.

We hope to hear from you again in the future at this Historic Building.

Gratefully yours,

Elder John C. Nelson
Visitors Center Director

Letter of praise from Elder John C. Nelson
St. George Temple and Visitors' Center Director
Used by permission.

About the Authors

Author Marilyn Arnold and composer Maurine Ozment

Marilyn Arnold

An Emeritus Professor of English at Brigham Young University, Marilyn Arnold served as Assistant to the President under Dallin H. Oaks and Dean of Graduate Studies under Jeffrey R. Holland.

A nationally known literary scholar, she has published widely in the academic world, as well as in Church publications. Marilyn is perhaps best known in Church circles for her classic work on the Book of Mormon, *Sweet Is the Word: Reflections on the Book of Mormon.* She also served as an associate editor of the *Book of Mormon Reference Companion*, and as a member of the editorial board for the *Journal of Book of Mormon Studies.* The author of eight published novels—one of them a national award winner—and several books of nonfiction, in 2003 she was honored as a Woman of Achievement by the governor's office in a special ceremony at the Utah State Capitol. In 2006 she received the Distinguished Citizen award from Dixie State College.

Maurine Ozment

Maurine Ozment, composer of the music for these hymns, is a lifelong teacher and adjudicator of piano performance. Having performed on concert stages and served on music faculties outside of Utah for many years, she now lives in southern Utah where she continues to perform and teach private students.

A much sought after accompanist and soloist, Maurine is also a published composer and arranger. Her compositions have been performed throughout the Church. Primary workers and children will recognize her as the composer of the popular "Hello Song" and "Feliz Cumpleaños." She regards composing the music for *Sacred Hymns of the Book of Mormon* as one of the high points of her life and career.

Lisa Farr

Lisa Farr is the daughter of Maurine Ozment, who wrote the music for these hymns. One of Lisa's hobbies began with transforming her mother's compositions from handwritten manuscript to publisher-ready printed text. She feels that all her years of experience in this work prepared her for this crowning project, *Sacred Hymns of the Book of Mormon.* A musician herself, Lisa is a pianist and accompanist. She has also done musical arrangements. Lisa is the wife of Tim Farr, a teacher and an accomplished performer of flute and guitar. In addition, Lisa has a passion for scouting; she has received awards and held important leadership positions in the Utah National Parks Council.

0 26575 52156 6